HANDBOOK OF THE
POTTERY & PORCELAIN
OF THE FAR EAST

IN THE DEPARTMENT OF
ORIENTAL ANTIQUITIES AND OF
ETHNOGRAPHY

FIG. 117. Covered jar: K'ang Hsi *famille noire*. H. 26 in.

HANDBOOK OF THE
POTTERY & PORCELAIN
OF THE FAR EAST

IN THE DEPARTMENT OF
ORIENTAL ANTIQUITIES AND OF
ETHNOGRAPHY

BY

R. L. HOBSON, C.B.

With 20 Plates and 260 Illustrations

738
B77h

PRINTED BY ORDER OF THE TRUSTEES

1937

PRINTED IN
GREAT BRITAIN
AT THE
UNIVERSITY PRESS
OXFORD
BY
JOHN JOHNSON
PRINTER
TO THE
UNIVERSITY

PREFACE TO SECOND EDITION

SINCE 1924, when the first edition of this handbook was issued, the Oriental Ceramic Collections have been enlarged by numerous gifts and purchases, the most important donations being those from the Keechong Hong, and from the collections of the Rev. J. F. Bloxam, M.C., Mr. H. B. Harris, Mr. Harvey Hadden, and Mr. Reginald Cory. The outstanding purchase is that of the Eumorfopoulos Collection, which, though not yet completed, has already greatly improved the representation of the early periods.

Much, too, has been added to our information about Far Eastern ceramics, chiefly by excavation in China, which is proceeding in a promising manner. Thus we have become acquainted with the prehistoric pottery of Honan and Kansu, the Shang-Yin wares of Anyang, and the products of Sung kilns in Honan, Chekiang, and Fukien. Moreover, the International Exhibition of Chinese Art[1] held at Burlington House in the winter of 1935–6 showed us many documentary specimens which throw further light on the subject.

With the growth of the Collections and widening information changes in the arrangement and labelling of the specimens are constantly needed; and as the positional references to objects in the cases tend to become rapidly obsolete, it has been decided to abandon them except where they are absolutely necessary. On the other hand, the present location of certain key specimens is given in a list printed on p. 175.

In preparing this second edition I have had valuable help from Mr. Henry Bergen in recasting parts of the Japanese pottery section.

R. L. HOBSON, C.B., *Keeper*,
DEPARTMENT OF ORIENTAL ANTIQUITIES
AND OF ETHNOGRAPHY.

November, 1936.

[1] Referred to for brevity's sake in the text as 'the Chinese Exhibition'.

PREFACE TO FIRST EDITION

THE Oriental Ceramic Collections, arranged in the eastern half of the ground-floor of the King Edward VII Galleries, illustrate the history of the potter's art in China, Corea, Japan, and parts of Indo-China. The wares made in all these regions are so intimately related that their treatment in one volume was manifestly desirable. The other Oriental wares, the pottery of the Near East, though not unaffected by the widespread influences of Chinese art, belong to a different culture. They will be treated in another Guide as the link between the ceramics of Asia and Mediterranean Europe.

The foundation of the entire exhibition, which is the subject of this Guide, is the collection formed by Sir Wollaston Franks in the fifth, sixth, and seventh decades of the nineteenth century. The Franks Collection was first exhibited as a loan in the Bethnal Green Museum, and it was then described in a catalogue issued in 1876 and 1878, and again, privately, in 1879. Since then it has been moved twice: first to the Asiatic Saloon in the British Museum where it remained till 1914, and after that to its present quarters where it was arranged after the European War and opened to the public in 1921.

The Franks Collection has a deservedly high reputation, not only for individual specimens of great rarity and merit, but because it was built up on scientific lines with the object of illustrating the whole story of Oriental ceramics. Unfortunately the early Chinese pottery was virtually unknown when the Collection was in the making: otherwise it would have been much stronger in that department. Almost all our knowledge of the early periods and almost all the specimens illustrating them have been acquired since 1900; and though many interesting, and some important documentary, examples have been secured, lack of funds has severely handicapped the Department in the competition for the more striking specimens. However, a useful series of the Han, T'ang, and Sung wares has been formed, and the Collection on the whole adequately fulfils its aim. It is certainly one of the best study collections in existence.

The wider knowledge of Chinese ceramic history, which has been gained since the end of the last century, has made it possible to adopt a chronological arrangement; and this has been done as far as circumstances allowed; but it will be found that structural difficulties have interfered here and there with details of sequence.

The general plan of the exhibition is as follows: Chinese pottery and early wares on the south side of the Gallery, and the porcelain of Kingtehchen and Tehwa, which means practically all the porcelain made in China from the Ming dynasty onward, on the north side. The Standard-cases in the centre have been used in the main for the larger objects which could not be conveniently fitted into the Pier-cases: incidentally they contain some of the most attractive specimens. The Corean, Siamese, and Japanese wares are arranged on the south side; and there is a small exhibition, following the Siamese wares, which illustrates special porcelains made in China for the Siamese and other foreign markets, and those showing foreign influence in form and decoration.

In preparing this Guide I have had valuable help from Mr. O. C. Raphael and the staff in the Ceramic section of the Department.

R. L. HOBSON, *Keeper,*
DEPARTMENT OF CERAMICS AND
ETHNOGRAPHY.

February, 1924.

CONTENTS

LIST OF ILLUSTRATIONS

INTRODUCTION

THE manufacture of earthenware is common to all ages and peoples, and the Chinese have no claims to priority either in the use of the potter's wheel or in the development of artistic pottery. Their successes date from the first millennium of our era, when the genius of the Chinese race asserted itself and pottery was made which for beauty of form and colouring has hardly an equal. But it was the discovery of porcelain that laid the world under an eternal debt to China, a debt which we acknowledge daily by the use of the word *china* as a general term for the finer ceramic wares. Our more specific word, porcelain, is of Italian origin and apparently derived from the Latin *porcellana*, a cowrie shell, the white translucent texture of which seemed to resemble that of the Chinese ware. The word is at least as old as Marco Polo who visited China in the thirteenth century, for it appears in his writings both in the sense of shell and of porcelain.

Chinese history does not record the name of an inventor, or the date of the invention, of porcelain; and we are content to assume that porcelain was gradually evolved by the potters of some favoured district who happened on the necessary materials in their search for clay. The nature of these materials (china clay and china stone) is discussed elsewhere, but we may say here that the analysis of some of the stoneware (cf. fig. 14) made in the third or fourth century of our era reveals the presence of china clay or kaolin. It does not follow that the secret of mixing china clay and china stone and of firing them at a sufficiently high temperature to make a vitrified white substance was at once discovered. Indeed there is every reason to think that the evolution was a very gradual one; but we can at any rate infer from Chinese writings that this secret was known in the sixth century; and we have definite and tangible evidence that the manufacture of porcelain had reached an advanced stage by the ninth. Some sinologues have attempted to arrive at the birthday of porcelain by tracing the first appearance in literature of the word *tz'ŭ*, which is freely used by Chinese writers to describe the porcelain of Kingtehchen: but even if this were possible, it would not settle the question, because the Chinese have never insisted on such a strict definition of the term as we have. To us porcelain is distinct from stoneware and pottery, and connotes something white, vitrified and translucent: whereas the Chinese apply the term *tz'ŭ* to opaque and dark-coloured bodies, provided they are hard and compact enough to emit a clear musical note on percussion. Many of the Sung wares are grey and even brown, but they are still *tz'ŭ* to the Chinese; and the pure white translucent ware of Kingtehchen is only one of many varieties of porcelain in the Chinese acceptation of the term. For earthenware, pure and simple, there is the term *wa*; and the more comprehensive *yao* (in Japanese, *yaki*) means a kiln and any sort of ware made in a kiln.

The development of the Chinese wares, both pottery and porcelain, and the growth of the diverse types of ornament can be traced in the pages of the Handbook. The Chinese are masters of colour decoration whether it be in the form of glazes, or of painting in underglaze blue or overglaze enamels: and there are few processes used by European porcelain manufacturers which have not been learnt from China. But there must often be something strange and unintelligible to the European mind in Chinese ceramic designs. The beautiful drawing of flowers, trees, and birds is readily understood and appreciated: but the repeated combinations of certain motives, the curious symbols, the quaint border patterns, and the strange mythical creatures demand an explanation. The whole subject of Chinese ornament is of absorbing interest; but to deal with it satisfactorily would require more space than is available here. We must confine ourselves to a few general remarks; and the curious are referred to more exhaustive works on the subject.

True Chinese ornament (e.g. that on porcelain made for native use) is never meaningless. The five-clawed dragon is the emblem of the Emperor, and the phoenix (*fêng*) that of the Empress: the lion, horse, and elephant are sacred to Buddha: the curious symbols are mostly of religious import; and the borders and diaper patterns are usually composed of emblematic shapes, such as the 'cloud and thunder' pattern (the key-fret), silkworm scrolls, 'cash' pattern and *ju-i* heads (i.e. the head of the *ju-i* staff which gives fulfilment to wishes). The cult of longevity is universal in China, and many of the decorative motives conceal allusions to it. Thus the stork, the tortoise, and the spotted deer are familiars of the God of Longevity; the pine tree, the *ling chih* fungus, the peach, and the gourd are emblems of long life, and there are hosts of *hsien* or beings who have found the secret of immortality.

Other blessings are also symbolized—happiness (*fu*) by the bat (*fu*) and the Buddha-hand citron: fertility by the pomegranate (*liu*): wedded bliss by a pair of mandarin ducks, or a pair of fishes: and literary success by a cassia bough, or a salmon leaping from waves. These allusive motives in porcelain decoration convey the implied good wish to the recipient of the porcelain. Still more numerous are the motives which have to be translated into words and phrases. In the Chinese language one sound has to do duty for several written characters, with the result that homophones are very numerous: as for instance *fu* (happiness), *fu* (a bat), *hung* (red), *hung* (vast). This circumstance gives scope for endless playing upon words and rebus making; and often the design on a piece of porcelain must be read as a rebus to be properly understood. Thus five red bats flying among cloud-scrolls can be interpreted as the good wish, *hung fu chih t'ien* 'vast happiness reaching the heavens!' Instances could easily be multiplied.

Then there are the numerous figure subjects, to explain which it would be necessary to plunge into history, romance, religion, and folk-lore. But enough has been said to show that much that seems strange and even grotesque in Chinese ornament has a meaning to those who are able to read it rightly. The designs on the porcelain made for export abroad are another matter. They are often confused and meaningless; and it would be waste of time to try to interpret them.

The most comprehensive Chinese works on ceramics are the *Ch'ing tê chên t'ao lu*, which was published in 1815 and translated by Stanislas Julien in his *Histoire et Fabrication de la Porcelaine Chinoise*, 1856; and the *T'ao shuo* which was published in 1774 and translated by S. W. Bushell in his *Description of Chinese Pottery and Porcelain*, 1910. With these may be classed the two long letters[1] written from Kingtehchen by the Jesuit Father d'Entrecolles in 1712 and 1722 and giving a very full account of the manufacture of porcelain as studied on the spot. These and other important materials have been collated in the more comprehensive publications such as Bushell's *Oriental Ceramic Art* (1899), and my own *Chinese Pottery and Porcelain* (1915), *Wares of the Ming Dynasty* (1923), and *Later Ceramic Wares of China* (1924); and this Handbook only attempts to summarize the information set out in these books so far as it is relevant to the Museum Collection, adding any fresh facts or theories which are necessary to bring it up to date. Among the various works consulted on Japanese Ceramics most use has been made of F. Brinkley's *Japan, Its History, Arts, and Literature*, vol. viii. For further information on Corean wares the reader is referred to the *Catalogue of the Le Blond Collection of Corean Pottery* by Bernard Rackham, 1918.

The illustrations in this Handbook are chiefly intended to exemplify types, but it will be noticed that monochromes are for the most part omitted. It was considered useless to attempt to represent monochromes by half-tone blocks; and indeed the lack of coloured reproductions is felt throughout. There are, however, sets of coloured postcards of the Chinese porcelain which help to make up this deficiency, and reference is made to them in the footnotes.

Another point which calls for explanation is the spelling of the Chinese place-names. In the great expanse of China there is room

---

[1] Printed *in extenso* at the end of Bushell's *Description of Chinese Pottery and Porcelain*.

for many dialects; and though a standardized pronunciation, known as Mandarin, is used over a large area in the north and among the educated classes in general, the language of the multitude differs widely in the several provinces, and place-names more than any other sounds are liable to be affected by the local patois. It has been customary for some time in romanizing the Chinese characters to use the Mandarin pronunciation for the sake of uniformity; but in dealing with place-names this method is inadequate and sometimes absurd. To take a single instance, the name of the Birmingham of the Canton Delta is pronounced *Fatshan*: the characters which compose it are pronounced in Mandarin *Fo* (or *Fu*) -*shan* (Buddha's hill); but it is unlikely that the name *Foshan* would be intelligible to a Cantonese. To get over such discrepancies, the Chinese Post Office has standardized the place-names in the *Postal Guide* on a system which takes full account of dialectical peculiarities. We have thus a uniform romanization of the name of every place which has a post office; and the list grows year by year. It is the only recognized authority to which we can refer, and it is obviously the one which will be generally accepted. The European student may be perplexed at first to find Yi-hsing spelt Ihing and Tz'ŭ Chou spelt Tzechow; but the transition stage is easily got over, and the Post Office spelling is now adopted in the Museum Ceramic Collections. Other Chinese characters are transliterated from the Mandarin pronunciation in the manner laid down by Wade.

THE PRINCIPAL CHINESE DYNASTIES

Hsia dynasty		2205–1766 B.C.
Shang (or Yin) dynasty		1766–1122 ,,
Chou ,,		1122–249 ,,
Ch'in ,,		221–206 ,,
Han ,,		206 B.C.–A.D. 220
The Six Dynasties		A.D. 220–589
[Including the Northern Wei		,, 386–535
,, Liang		,, 502–556]
Sui dynasty		,, 589–618
T'ang dynasty		,, 618–906
The Five Dynasties		,, 907–960
Sung dynasty		,, 960–1279
Yüan ,,		,, 1260–1368
Ming ,,		,, 1368–1644
Ch'ing ,,		,, 1644–1912

CHINESE POTTERY

HAN DYNASTY AND EARLIER

(BAY III and STANDARD-CASE C)

THE earliest specimens in the Collections are two painted urns from Kansu presented by the Östasiatiska Samlingarna of Stockholm. Prof. J. G. Andersson's discoveries[1] first in Honan and Manchuria and then in Kansu have established the existence of a well-developed pottery technique at a period which has been tentatively fixed as from 3500 to 1700 B.C.

The two urns (fig. 1) which are assigned to the first half of the third millennium B.C. are of a well-made reddish-buff ware, of pleasing form and decorated with boldly drawn patterns in red, black, and purplish brown. They belong to a group of painted pottery which is closely related in style to the neolithic pottery found in Western Asia, at Anau, Susa, Ur, in Southern Persia and Baluchistan, and at Tripolje in Southern Russia. The relationship between these two groups in the East and West is too obvious to be ignored, even if it cannot yet be satisfactorily explained; but this enigmatic painted pottery seems to have disappeared before the Shang dynasty (1766–1122 B.C.) and to have had little or no influence on the development of Chinese ceramics.

Prof. Andersson places in an earlier stage (3500–3000 B.C.) another group of plain ware with simple incised or pricked patterns and impressions of coarse fabric or matting. We have no specimens of this less sophisticated neolithic ware; but we recognize its descendants in the Chou pottery (fig. 2) of which some interesting examples are exhibited in Bay III. Meanwhile there is a hint of a fine ware made at Anyang in the Shang-Yin period. To-day it is represented by a few fragments of soft white pottery vessels decorated with raised designs similar in style and appearance to those of the Shang-Yin bronzes, carved ivories and bones.

The pottery of the Han dynasty (206 B.C.–A.D. 220) is more adequately represented. The best-authenticated specimens are those obtained by the Rev. Th. Torrance from tombs which he visited personally in Szechwan[a] and which were in some cases dated by coins and inscriptions.

[1] J. G. Andersson, *Palaeontologia Sinica*, Series D, vol. i, Peking, 1923; *Memoirs of the Geological Survey of China*, Series A, No. 5, June 1925, Preliminary Report on Archaeological Research in Kansu; and Nils Palmgren, *Palaeontologia Sinica*, Series D, vol. iii, fasc. 1, Peking, 1934.

FIG. 2. Goblet. Chou dynasty. H. 6·6 in.

FIG. 1. Urn from Kansu. 3rd millennium B.C. H. 12 in.

The Chinese practice was to bury with the dead models of his family, retinue, domestic animals, implements, utensils, and even ornaments so that his spirit might be provided as fully as possible with all the things which had interested him in life. Naturally the quantity and quality of the tomb furniture varied with the status and wealth of the family concerned. The Szechwan pottery in Bay III would appear to have come from poor men's tombs. It is for the most part roughly made and unpretentious, but it teaches us what to expect in the Han graves, e.g. a coffin

FIG. 3. Bricks from a Han tomb in Szechwan. L. of largest 16·5 in.

encased in ornamented bricks, a tray with vessels for food and drinking, a model of a stove, figures of women and attendants, poultry, &c. A few of the pieces such as the coffin bricks and the figure of a woman with a child on her back have considerable artistic merit (figs. 3 and 4). The interesting series[b] of tomb figures, &c., found by the ill-fated Lieut. J. W. Brooke in his expedition in the Lolo country in Szechwan, are also of the Han period (fig. 5).

All these objects are unglazed and mostly of a slaty grey pottery, made on the wheel or shaped in moulds. More elaborate decoration of pottery is seen on the slabs and bricks in Bay III and on the pillar (fig. 6)—all of them covered with a variety of stamped ornaments which are worthy of study—and on the vases with painted designs in unfired pigments. One of these latter, with formal designs, is probably as old as the Han dynasty: another, delightfully painted with a frieze of hunting demon figures, animals, and a rising crane, though slightly later, has special interest as a very early example of Chinese brush work (fig. 10).

Of the remaining specimens the majority are glazed. The ware of these pieces is a reddish pottery and the glaze, a lead-silicate, has a natural warm yellowish tone which over the red produces a brown colour. It is, however, in most cases coloured with oxide of copper, and a fine leaf-green is the result. These

FIG. 4. Unglazed figure. Han dynasty. H. 7·7 in.

FIG. 5. Pottery head from a Han tomb in Szechwan. H. 8·6 in.

brown and green glazes rarely appear intact. Their long sojourn in the earth has induced decay, and the surface is generally encrusted with an iridescent layer which assumes beautiful gold and silver lustres. It is glaze that makes porous earthenware able to hold liquids and so fit for domestic use; and the introduction of glaze marks a turning-point in the development of pottery. When this point was reached in China is not yet certain. A kind of gloss seen on some of the reputed Shang-Yin pottery found at Anyang may well have been an accident of the kiln. Such a gloss caused by wood ashes falling on the heated pottery is seen on the early Corean wares and the pottery found in the Japanese dolmens.

In the International Exhibition of Chinese Art at Burlington
House, 1935–6, there was a covered jar (No. 454 in the Catalogue)
decorated with relief ornament in late Chou style and coated
with a green lead glaze. Unless this is an archaizing piece it
points to the use of the lead glaze at a period not later than

FIG. 6. Ornamental brick. Han dynasty. H. 31 in.

the third century B.C. But there is no specimen of glazed pottery
in the Collections to which could be safely given a date earlier
than Han.

The more usual methods of decorating the Han pottery, when
decoration was used, were incising or stamping small ornaments,
or moulding reliefs either on the ware itself or on pads or strips
of clay which were attached by means of liquid clay. Good
examples of these moulded and applied ornaments are seen in
the covers of the 'hill jar' (fig. 9) and 'hill censer' with a design
of hills rising from waves, from which they derive their names;

FIGS. 7, 8, and 9. Well jar, wine vase (H. 12·3 in.) and hill jar: glazed Han pottery.

and in the handsome wine-jar (fig. 8) which has two tiger-mask handles, obviously derived from a bronze, and a belt of typical Han ornament, a frieze of demons and animals, the hunters and

Fig. 10. Unglazed vase painted with pigments: probably 3rd century. H. 13·6 in.

the hunted, spaced by wave designs. Occasionally the green or brown colour of the glaze on these wares is diversified by dots and stripes of coloured clay.

It will be seen that the Han potters were not always content with making literal copies of the objects which they wished to represent in the tomb furniture. Some of their most attractive

FIG. 11. Black unglazed vase. Han
dynasty. H. 16·25 in.

FIG. 12. Glazed watch-tower.
Han dynasty. H. 34 in.

FIG. 13. Black unglazed vase. Probably Han. H. 11·4 in.

models are skilfully conventionalized so as to assume an ornamental form. A pigsty, a rice-mill, and some of the cooking
stoves, are very literal renderings; and the 'well jar' (fig. 7),
with all the mechanism of the well—the pulley protected by a
pent-house, &c., and even the pitcher on the brim—naturally
assumes an ornamental form. On the other hand, a flat model
of a stove with implements and food moulded in relief is a clever
adaptation; and the 'granary urns' with their three bear-shaped
feet and roofed tops, are happy conventionalizations of the
granary tower.

It will be noticed, too, that many of the utensils and vases,
the hill censer and hill jar and other ornamental forms, are
designed after bronze models. This is only natural, as the bronze-
worker's art in China was at this period far in advance of the
potter's; and in some cases the pottery vessels were evidently
made for burial purposes, as cheap substitutes for bronze.

HAN TO T'ANG

(A.D. 221–618)

(*BAY III and STANDARD-CASE C*)

WITH the fall of the Han dynasty the great Chinese Empire
split up into warring principalities, and it was not again firmly
united until the seventh century. The ceramic history of this
long interval of four centuries is obscure, but much of the so-
called proto-porcelain[1] must belong to this period, though it
may have originated in the Han dynasty or even earlier. This
is a hard greyish ware, apparently containing kaolin in an
impure state, with an olive-brown glaze.[2] A typical specimen
is seen in fig. 14, a small, neatly formed vase, with bands of
incised ornament on the shoulder and two loop handles. The
slender vase with Zodiac animals in relief is a later representative
of the same family. A softer glaze of deep brown colour appears
on a fine model of an ox-cart which is reputed to be of the Sui
period.[3]

The tomb wares of the time are mostly of a dark grey pottery,
unglazed but pigmented; and the figurines are often distinguished
by spirited modelling and a certain quaint humour.

It is reasonable to suppose that the well-known Han types

[1] See Berthold Laufer, *Beginnings of Porcelain in China*, Chicago, 1917.
[2] A glaze of this type occurs on pottery fragments with stamped designs of
late Chou type found on Lamma Island, near Hong Kong: see D. J. Finn,
in the *Hong Kong Naturalist*, vol. vi, nos. 3 and 4, Dec. 1935.
[3] A Sui grave excavated at Anyang yielded porcellanous stoneware vessels
with a yellowish glaze. See Cat., Chinese Exhibition, No. 634.

continued to be made for part at least of the interval and that
the art which reached such a high pitch in the T'ang dynasty
was in process of development during the latter part. We are

FIG. 14. Vase with greenish-brown glaze:
3rd or 4th century. H. 7·8 in.

FIG. 15. Unglazed figure:
Northern Wei dynasty. H.
14·3 in.

prepared to find that much at present grouped as Han and
T'ang really belongs to this no-man's land, and we are only
awaiting evidence from scientific excavations to point the way
to a more correct distribution of our collections.

THE T'ANG DYNASTY

(A.D. 618–906)

(*STANDARD-CASE D and TABLE-CASE IN BAY IV*)

STANDARD-CASE D is filled with pottery of various types which
is assigned to the T'ang period. Some of it may be a little earlier
and some a little later, but there are good reasons for regarding
most of it as T'ang, even if these reasons are largely based on
deductions rather than circumstantial evidence. Among the very

few demonstrably T'ang specimens in existence are those in the Shoso-in at Nara, in Japan, which have been preserved there since the eighth century. They are a few pieces of pottery with the glaze mottled with green and yellow. Pottery of this kind must have been in very general use, as we find obvious imitations of it among the fragments unearthed on the ninth-century site of

Fig. 17. Dish with coloured glaze. T'ang dynasty. D. 11·3 in.

Samarra on the Tigris. The same mottled glaze is seen on the well-modelled figures, human and animal, which have been found in reputed T'ang graves in China. Had one such tomb been scientifically excavated we should have evidence as satisfactory as that of Nara, for it was customary, in important burials at any rate, to place an engraved slab in the tomb recording the history of the dead. Rubbings of such slabs and even the slabs themselves have been brought over to Europe, but, unfortunately, separated from the reputed contents of the tombs and with nothing but a verbal assertion to connect them. One of these slabs commemorated a princely personage of the name Wên Shou-ch'êng who died in A.D. 683 and another Liu T'ing-hsün who died in 728.[1]

These accounts are probably correct, though the evidence supporting them is defective, and, in any case, the remarkable figures associated with Wên and Liu would undoubtedly be ascribed to the T'ang period on the analogy of their mottled glazes with those of the Nara speci-

mens. The hundreds of graves exposed by railway construction have given us ample material to work on, and using the Nara wares as a starting-point it has been possible to build up a considerable T'ang series and to formulate many of the characteristics of T'ang pottery. Tracing these analogies from one type to another is a fascinating pursuit, but there is only space in this Handbook for a summary of the results.

The T'ang grave wares are usually of a white or pale buff material, varying from a soft plaster-like earthenware to a hard stoneware or porcelain. Often they are unglazed, but coated with a white slip and decorated with painted patterns in unfired pigments—black, red, and occasionally blue. When glaze is used on the soft earthenware, it is a soft lead-silicate. It is transparent and of a slightly yellowish cast; and when positive colour was required, the colouring agent was applied in dabs or washes on the body of the ware and absorbed into the glaze

Fig. 18. Bottle with coloured glaze. T'ang dynasty. H. 9·7 in.

which was subsequently laid over it. The colours used were pale green, leaf green, amber yellow, cobalt blue, and very rarely a violet or aubergine. All these colours are found as monochromes as well as in mottled combinations or in separate washes. Some of the glazes used in the harder T'ang wares are much more refractory and evidently felspathic; their colours include white, a watery green of celadon type, true celadon, black, and chocolate brown. The last mentioned is sometimes splashed with a variegated glaze of blue and grey, the colours in which are probably accidental. It will be seen that the potter's art had developed much since the Han period.

[1] A splendid set of large figures associated with the latter has come to the Museum with the Eumorfopoulos Collection.[c]

PLATE II

Fig. 16. Camel with coloured glaze. T'ang dynasty. H. 33 in.

The decoration of the T'ang wares is also much advanced. Moulded designs and applied reliefs formed by moulds or stamps were used with great skill and taste, though in the same fashion as in the Han period: but the method of engraving a design in outline and filling it in with coloured glazes was new; and so too were 'graining', or marbling, and painting in liquid clay or slip. The T'ang potters made full use of different slips to variegate their wares. There are, moreover, some minor characteristics of the T'ang pottery, such as the flat base with bevelled edge (a common, though not an invariable, feature) and the economical application of the glaze which ends in a wavy line some distance short of the base. With regard to the T'ang forms, those made on the wheel are finely proportioned with singularly beautiful lines; and it will be noticed that there is a decided suggestion of Hellenistic influence both in the form and ornament of some of the wares. The amphora-shaped vases with their two serpent handles obviously follow a Greek tradition; and honeysuckle pattern, palmettes, and leaf and tongue borders are a few of the many decorations which show classical influence; while the piping boys

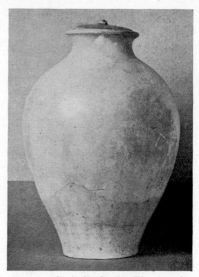

FIG. 19. Grain jar from a T'ang tomb. H. 13 in.

FIG. 20. Glazed T'ang flask. H. 4·8 in.

in vine scrolls on fig. 20 are frankly Hellenistic. A cup-shaped mouth is common on many of the T'ang bottles and vases; and so are small rudimentary handles, usually loop-shaped and applied to the shoulders; and a frequently occurring type of ornament is the applied pads stamped with palmette designs or floral arabesques or sometimes simple rosettes. The more elabor-

FIGS. 21 and 22. Actor (H. 11·4 in.) and lady (H. 12 in.).
Unglazed T'ang figures.

ate specimens are decorated with finely drawn designs with out-lines incised and filled in with washes of colour (fig. 17).

On the west side of Standard-case D is an interesting series of figures and vessels which were obtained by a railway engineer from a tomb disturbed by a railway cutting near Honanfu. This funeral outfit includes six covered jars (fig. 19), probably intended for the six kinds of grain; a wine-vase of amphora shape with cup-shaped mouth and serpent handles; a circular tray on which stood a small melon-shaped pot surrounded by shallow cups; a series of figures, a lady on horse-back, attendants

PLATE III

FIG. 25. Glazed figure: from a tomb in Szechwan, dated 839. H. 9·5 in.

male and female, priestly persons, a long-nosed man of foreign appearance, and six mail-clad 'life-guards'; a number of animals, horses, camels, pigs, sheep, a dog, and a goose; and two supernatural creatures, with horned human heads on bull bodies, known as *t'u kuai* (earth spirits) whose function was to guard the grave. The figures are of the usual white plaster-like material with pale, straw-coloured glaze, and the vases are of a hard white ware with transparent glaze of faint greenish tint, minutely crackled.

FIGS. 23 and 24. Sphinx of glazed pottery (L. 5·4 in.) and another, gilt: 9th century.

A considerable variety of T'ang wares is shown in the other parts of the Case. There are some well-modelled figures, human and animal, among which two female figures and an actor (figs. 21 and 22) are noteworthy. One of them is well decorated with red and black pigments.

There are specimens of the coloured lead-silicate glazes, including a monochrome yellow jar and a strangely renaissance-like ewer with a rare blue monochrome glaze. The latter, which is unfortunately damaged, came from a tomb in Honan. The tall figure of a Lokapala, or guardian of one of the quarters of the Buddhist Heaven, has a brilliant mottled glaze; and a large figure of a camel has a splashed yellow glaze[d].

Three figures, a bearded man seated and two sphinx-like creatures (figs. 23–25), are of peculiar interest. They were obtained by the Rev. Th. Torrance from a tomb in Szechwan and with them was an inscribed slab which showed that the tomb was that of 'His Excellency Ts'ui' who died in 839.

It will be noticed at once that these specimens differ considerably from the familiar types of T'ang pottery such as those found in the tomb of Liu T'ing-hsün (p. 12); but that is not surprising, for they are more than a century later and made in a remote province. The seated figure and one of the sphinxes are very similar in technique. Both have a soft red body and a transparent lead glaze of yellowish cast. By the use of slip and copper oxide several distinct colours have been produced on this surface—an orange red (glaze over the red body), a cream white (glaze over

Fig. 27. Glazed tomb figure: 10th century. H. 10·2 in.

Fig. 28. T'ang porcelain ewer. H. 15·5 in.

a wash of white slip), light leaf-green (the same with a tinge of copper oxide in the glaze) and a brown which might have been formed by the glaze with a tinge of copper-green over the red body without any wash of white slip. The seated figure is one of great dignity; and, though obviously made in a mould, it has more individuality than is customary in the standardized types of tomb figures. The man-headed animal, or sphinx, is of unusual form; and its companion piece has other unfamiliar features. Though made of precisely the same ware and shaped in the same manner, it is perhaps unique in being lacquered over with gold.

By far the noblest ceramic statue in the Museum is the large seated figure of a Lohan. It is attributed to the T'ang period

PLATE IV

Fig. 26. T'ang ewer with black glaze. H. 10·9 in.

for reasons given in the illustrated monograph which is on sale in the Gallery and on the bookstalls.

There are a few specimens of the harder T'ang glazes, including a ewer with porcellanous body and black glaze (fig. 26) and one or two pieces of white porcelain (fig. 28); but the most interesting objects of this group are shown in the Window-case of Bay IV. These include fragments of white and creamy-white porcelain found on the ninth-century site of Samarra on the Tigris, together with fragments of green-glazed porcellanous ware known

FIG. 30. Yüeh ware water-pot. 10th century. H. 4·5 in.

as celadon (see p. 21). It is thus definitely established that wares of these advanced types were not only made in China in the T'ang dynasty but actually exported to foreign countries.

It seems probable that the porcelain of this period was mainly white and celadon green. This is borne out by the few passages in Chinese literature which mention the material. The eighth-century Classic of Tea gives the palm for tea bowls to the factories of Yüeh Chou and Hsing Chou, the former in Chekiang and the latter in Southern Chihli. The Yüeh Chou bowls were described as green and comparable with ice and jade, the Hsing Chou bowls as white like snow or silver. Five other potteries are named as producing tea bowls but of inferior quality; and among them was Hung Chou, the modern Nanchang, in Kiangsi, in the very district in which the famous porcelain centre of Kingtehchen is situated. Yet another factory is named in a poem by Tu Fu

(712–770), viz. Tayi, between Chengtu and Kiungchow in Szechwan, which produced bowls, 'light but strong, and surpassing the hoar-frost and snow in whiteness'.

The kilns in which the so-called Yüeh ware was made have been located at Yü-yáo Hsien, about 40 miles east of Shaohsing (formerly Yüeh Chou) in Chekiang, and there are fragments and wasters[e] from the site in the Collection, from which a few complete specimens such as fig. 30 have been identified. The ware is a grey porcellanous stoneware and the glaze olive-green of varying intensity. Apart from the short period (see below) when it was reserved for the princes of Wu and Yüeh, the ware was widely disseminated; and many fragments of it have been found in the waste heaps of Fostat, at Samarra, Ctesiphon, and in other parts of Western Asia. The factories were evidently active in the T'ang dynasty and they continued as late as the Southern Sung period.

THE FIVE DYNASTIES

(A.D. 907–60)

WE have little information about the pottery made under the Five Dynasties which filled the interval of fifty-three years between the T'ang and the Sung. The most celebrated types were the *pi sê* ware of Yüeh Chou and the *Ch'ai* ware.

The expression *pi sê* (secret, or private, colour) dates from the period between 907 and 976 when the princes of Wu and Yüeh, who reigned at Hangchow, reserved the so-called Yüeh ware for their personal use. The Ch'ai ware, 'blue as the sky after rain', was made at Chengchow in Honan and named Ch'ai after the family name of Shih Tsung of the posterior Chou dynasty, who reigned from 954 to 959. It was only made for royal use and no authenticated specimen is at present known, although various attempts have been made to arrive at its identification by deductions from the rather poetical Chinese descriptions of its qualities.

THE SUNG DYNASTY

(A.D. 960–1279)

(BAY IV)

DURING the long reign of the Sung Emperors (960 to 1279) the arts of peace, and among them the potter's, flourished exceedingly. There were numerous potteries scattered over the eighteen provinces of China; and five or six of these have been described by historians in sufficient detail to enable us to identify the types

PLATE V

FIG. 29. Fragments from the Yü-yao kiln-sites

of ware made in them and in a few cases their actual productions.
Some random excavations made on the kiln-sites have put us
into possession of further information; and it is clear that if
systematic excavation on the known sites were undertaken,
we should be able to classify the Sung wares with considerable
exactitude.

Speaking generally, the Sung wares are mostly porcellanous,
either an actual translucent, white porcelain or a highly vitrified
ware of very similar nature. The Chinese themselves do not
trouble to make a distinction between these types; and if the
ware is compact and hard and rings with a musical note when
struck, it is classed by them as porcelain, even though the body
be dark-coloured and opaque, and of a type which we should
regard as stoneware. The glazes are thick, as befitted the body,
high-fired and felspathic; and they are distinguished by many
subtle and delicate shades of colour partly due to opalescence
and partly to colouring agents such as iron and copper. Evenness
of colour was a quality highly prized at this period; and the
broken tints, mixed colours and *flambé* glazes, though greatly
admired to-day, were of less account in Sung times.

The decoration of the superior types of ware was in moulded
or applied relief, carved or incised on the body and visible through
the translucent glaze; but decoration was not a necessity for the
finer Sung forms and the monochrome glazes needed no embellishment. Much attention was paid to forms; and, if they were
not always as simple and spontaneous as those of the T'ang
pottery, it was because the fashion of the time favoured the
reproduction of old bronze shapes, which called for the use of
complicated moulds.

The most noted Sung wares are the Ju, Kuan, Ko, Chün,
Lungchüan and Ting, to which may be added the Chien, and
the Tzechow wares.

The *Ju* was an Imperial ware made by potters from Juchow
for about twenty years at the beginning of the twelfth century
in the Imperial precincts at Kaifeng.

The *T'ao lu* quotes this account from the *Ch'ing po tsa chih*, which
was written in 1193, and which adds that the Imperial Ju ware was
already scarce.

In the old Peking palace collection there is a small group of
specimens traditionally attributed to the Ju factory; and as it is
on record that in 1728 Ju ware vessels were sent from the Palace
to Kingtehchen to be copied, the attribution is evidently one of
long standing. The dish (fig. 31), which is inscribed with a poem
written by the Emperor Ch'ien Lung, once belonged to this
group and shows its quite distinctive character. It is made of
buff stoneware and has a thick, opaque glaze of pale lavender
tint, which has unfortunately suffered some discoloration in a

fire. The base rim is slightly splayed and on the base are five small oval spur marks.

The Chinese Government sent a good series of these wares to the International Exhibition in London and they all conformed to this general type, with slight variations in the glaze which in some cases had a greenish tint and as a rule was lightly crackled.

Fig. 31. Ju ware dish. Sung. D. 7·25 in.

The identification of the Ju ware has long been a problem. When the first edition of this Guide was written another theory held the field, viz. that the so-called *ying ch'ing* ware (see p. 36) represented the Ju type. In view of the large quantities of the *ying ch'ing* ware which have been unearthed in all parts of China this theory can no longer be seriously considered, and we see in this small, choice group illustrated by fig. 31 a much more probable identification of the rare Ju ware.

Kuan ware, as the name implies, is another of the 'Official' or 'Imperial' wares made primarily for the use of the court. According to Chinese accounts it was first made for a short time

PLATE VI

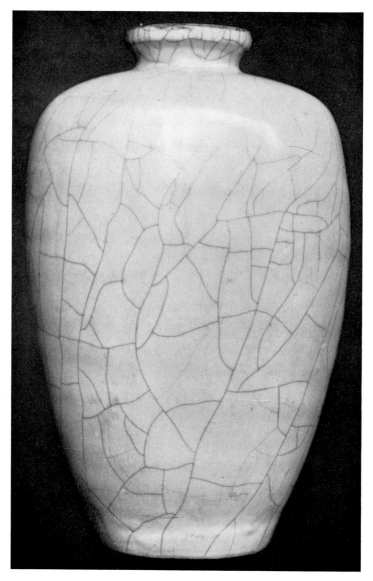

Fig. 32. Kuan ware vase. Sung. H. 10·75 in.

PLATE VII

Fig. 33. Fragments from the Altar kiln-site, Hangchow

at Kaifeng at the beginning of the twelfth century; and when the Sung Emperor was driven south of the Yangtze in 1127 by the Tartar invasion, kilns were set up at Hangchow, the new capital, first in the palace enclosure below the Phoenix Hill and afterwards near the Altar of Heaven (*ch'iao tan*). The ware of the latter kilns is stated to have resembled that of the former but to have been somewhat inferior to it. Search has been made for the sites of these kilns, but those of the Phoenix Hill factory have not yet been located. On the other hand, the Altar of Heaven kiln-site has been found. It is strewn with fragments and wasters and the remains of seggars, i.e. fire-clay cases in which the ware was baked. There is a good series of fragments from this site in the Collections (fig. 33) and they tell us what the Altar Kuan ware, and by inference the Phoenix Hill Kuan, was like. These fragments have a greyish black body, neatly potted and often remarkably thin, and a thick, rather opaque, glaze of delicate dove grey or greenish grey colour, crackled and un-crackled. Some notable specimens of the Altar Kuan were lent by the Chinese Government to the International Exhibition at Burlington House. The bottle (fig. 34) is probably a specimen of this ware; while the vase (fig. 32) and a peach-shaped cup from the Eumorfopoulos Collection are perhaps from the Phoenix Hill kilns.

Ko ware. What is known as Ko ware is another dark-bodied ware which is so like the Kuan ware that it might well be a variety of the latter with a rather browner body and a glaze slightly more glassy and more obviously full of bubbles. In colour the two wares are very similar, but the Ko is always covered with a clearly defined and rather regular crackle. The specimen illustrated by fig. 35 has a greyish green glaze, and on the base is inscribed *pao yung* (precious for use).

The Chinese tradition is that Ko ware was first made by the elder (*ko*) of the two Chang brothers who lived at Lungchüan in Chekiang at the end of the Southern Sung period. So far no trace of a dark-bodied ware has been found on the kiln-sites of the Lungchüan district.

Lungchüan ware. The district of Lungchüan, in the prefecture of Chuchow in the south of the province of Chekiang, was noted from very early times for the manufacture of a beautiful porcel-lanous ware with grey-green glaze which is generally known in Europe as celadon. According to a passage in the *T'ao-lu* the district was celebrated for this class of ware as early as the beginning of the Sung dynasty; and it is possible that the industry was in full activity many years before that date, for fragments of a celadon, barely distinguishable from the Lung-chüan ware, were found on the ninth-century site of Samarra, on the Tigris. Indeed, it is likely that the earliest coloured

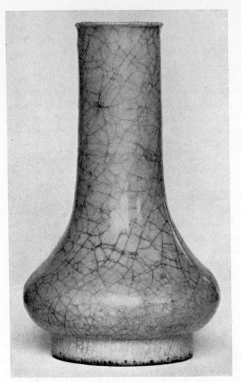

Fig. 34. Altar Kuan bottle. Sung. H. 9 in.

Fig. 35. Ko ware bowl. Sung. D. 8·25 in.

porcelain was of the celadon type, the potters' aim being to imitate the appearance of the much-prized green jade.

The Lungchüan celadon has a greyish white porcellanous body (it tends to brown where the raw edges have been touched by the fire of the kiln) and a thick smooth glaze varying in colour from grass-green to grey, but usually of a cool sea-green tint. The colour is due to the presence of iron, but it was perhaps

FIG. 36. Sung celadon dish. D. 16 in.

assisted in some cases by a tinge of cobalt blue. As a rule the celadon is stoutly built, strong and heavy, a ware admirably suited for the export trade. But there were finer varieties which were too highly prized by the Chinese to find their way overseas. The best of these were made by the Chang family which worked beneath the Liu-hua hill at Lungchüan, at the end of the Sung period. They were lighter and thinner than the ordinary celadons, and the glaze of the finest specimens was distinguished by a delicate shade of bluish grey. The Japanese have always prized it highly and it is now generally known as *kinuta* celadon from a famous *kinuta* (mallet)-shaped specimen preserved in Japan. Good examples of the stronger sea-green celadons (fig. 36) in a variety of shapes and shades are shown in Bay IV.· The decoration of the Lungchüan celadon wares is carved or incised on the body, moulded, or applied in small reliefs which are sometimes left without a covering of glaze. When this last happens, the unprotected 'biscuit' usually burns a reddish-brown in the firing. A large trade was done in this ware in medieval times by land and sea in Persia, India, Arabia, Egypt, and West Africa, and on the coasts of the Mediterranean; and it was much prized in the

FIG. 37. Lungchüan bulb bowl. Sung. D. 11·25 in.

Near East for its strength and beauty not less than for the curious superstition that it would disclose the presence of poison in any food served up on it. Two dishes in Bay IV were found respectively at Khartum and Rhodes; and in the collections of fragments there are pieces of celadon found on a score of ancient sites along the routes of medieval Eastern trade. A stem-cup[f], with rusty brown spots in the celadon glaze, is a specimen of the rare spotted celadon, the *tobi seiji* of the Japanese.

It has been stated in Chinese books that the potters transferred their industry to Chuchow in the Ming dynasty and that the manufacture in this district was abandoned at the end of that period; but recent excavations on the kiln-sites of the Lungchüan district prove both these statements to be only partially true.

There were other districts where wares of the celadon type were made. Ch'ên-liu and other localities in the neighbourhood of Kaifeng in Honan produced a highly prized variety in the Sung period known as *tung ch'ing* ware. It is mentioned in several Chinese works and the description clearly points to a celadon type, but no specimens have yet been definitely located. On the other hand, there is a large and important group of celadons with a brownish buff stoneware body and olive green glaze, very similar to that of the Yüeh ware, which is generally described as Northern Chinese celadon and may be a variety of the *tung ch'ing* ware of Honan. Much of it comes from tombs

FIG. 38. 'Northern celadon' ewer. Sung. H. 8·7 in.

and excavations in the north of China and it has been found in the Koryu tombs at Songdo in Corea. A dish (fig. 39) and a ewer (fig. 38) will serve to illustrate this ware which has close affinities in form and decoration to the *ying ch'ing* porcelain (see p. 36).

The singularly beautiful bowl (fig. 40) with fine, porcellanous body and a bluish green glaze is obviously a superior Sung ware; but it differs in material from any of the known Sung types and the suggestion that it may be a variety of *tung ch'ing* ware is merely a conjecture, reached by a process of elimination.

Celadon was certainly made at Kingtehchen in the Ming dynasty and later. This variety is distinguished by its white porcelain body. The celadon glaze is also reputed to have been

Fig. 39. 'Northern celadon' dish. Sung. D. 5·6 in.

Fig. 40. Bowl with bluish green glaze. Sung dynasty. D. 9·5 in.

used on the Kwangtung stoneware, especially on figures which have the fleshy parts in red biscuit; but the origin of this belief is obscure, and it seems more probable that such fine specimens, at any rate, as the shrine dated 1406 are of Chekiang make.

Chün ware. The thick, greyish glaze of some of the Kuan ware has obvious affinities with the Chün glazes which appear on an important and better-understood group. Chün ware was originally made at Chün Chou, the modern Yühsien, which lies south-west of Kaifeng in Honan. The body varies widely in fineness and the Chinese distinguish two groups which they call *tz'ŭ t'ai* (porcelain body) and *sha t'ai* (sandy body). The former is represented by the beautiful bulb-bowl which has a greyish porcellanous body of fine grain (fig. 41); and the latter by a number of bowls[g] and other objects which have bodies varying from a dark grey stoneware to buff and brick-red earthenware.

It is recorded that the Chün Chou factories supplied flower-pots and stands to the Sung court. These Imperial Chün wares would doubtless be of the finer material, and like the bulb-bowl just mentioned, covered with opalescent glaze with a fine play of colour. The Chün glazes are very varied and Chinese descriptions of them make quite a considerable list—including rose-purple, cherry apple red, aubergine purple, plum bloom, millet colour, sky blue, and mottled. As we know them, they are mostly lavender-grey or greenish grey dappled, splashed, shot or diffused with a purple which is now bluish, now crimson. It appears that copper oxide was used to some small extent as a colouring agent, but most of the varied play of colours is due to the opalescence of a thick bubbly glaze. A wash of ferruginous clay, which appears as olive-brown glaze on the base, usually completes the covering of the finer Chün, and a numeral, ranging from 1 to 10, to indicate the size, is almost always incised on the base or foot. Irregular and V-shaped lines or partings in the glaze are often noticed on the Chün wares and are called 'earth-worm marks' by native connoisseurs who regard them as signs of genuineness.

Next in quality to these numbered Chün wares are specimens like fig. 42, which have a grey porcellanous body and a beautiful lavender-grey glaze usually splashed or suffused with purple. The splashes often assume pictorial forms—suggesting fruit, butterflies, bats, dragons, Chinese characters, &c.—and they are evidently intentional, though Chinese writers speak of them as *yao pien* or furnace transmutations. This type of Chün ware appears in greater variety of forms than the first-mentioned.

The coarser (*sha t'ai*) Chün wares which comprise bowls, dishes, jars, incense burners, and occasionally vases, pillows, &c., are fairly well represented in the Collection by whole specimens and fragments. The glazes are chiefly a variety of opalescent greys and lavenders, almost always mottled or splashed with purple; but on the coarser body they are usually less vivid in colour.

A large number of kiln-sites have been found in Northern Honan strewn with fragments and wasters of the Chün type. In fact the manufacture seems to have been very general throughout the whole district which lies within a radius of about 100 miles from Honanfu. The Collection includes numerous fragments from these sites and an interesting example of a bowl still in its original seggar.

There is also a bulb-bowl with 'three-colour' glazes of Ming

FIG. 42. Chün ware water-pot. Sung. H. 3·6 in.

type (turquoise, yellow, and aubergine) which is reputed to have been found on the site of the Chün Chou kilns.[h] There is literary evidence that the industry survived at least as late as the sixteenth century, and this bulb-bowl suggests that the Chün potters made some effort to meet the change of fashion in the Ming dynasty.

There is another Chün type to which the term *sha t'ai* applies very aptly, for it has a buff body of sandy appearance. The glaze, which has a waxen appearance, is very thick, opalescent, and minutely crackled and usually of an even lavender-blue or lavender-turquoise colour. Flushes and well-defined splashes of purple not infrequently diversify the glaze; but the general impression is that the colour has greater solidity than that of the Chün types previously described. This type of ware is distinguished as *ma chün* by Chinese connoisseurs, who explain that it was first made by a potter named Ma; much of it clearly

PLATE VIII

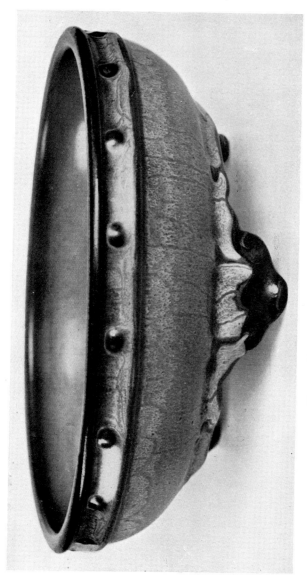

Fig. 41. Bulb-bowl of Sung Chün ware. D. 7·4 in.

belongs to the Ming period. The two-handled vase (fig. 43) is a remarkably fine specimen of this ware. It has a sandy buff body which has burnt red at the edges, and a thick lavender-turquoise glaze, with flecks of crimson on the neck and shoulders.

The Chün types were freely imitated at later dates and in various places. A potter named Ou who worked at Ihing at the end of the Ming period specialized in Chün glazes, and he doubtless had many followers. One would expect the Ihing

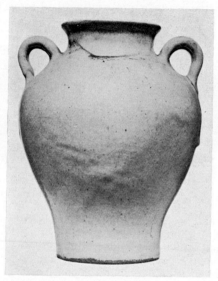

FIG. 43. Vase of 'Ma Chün' ware. H. 10·3 in.

Chün wares to have a stoneware body similar to that of the teapots in Bay V.

There are also Kwangtung wares with glazes of similar Chün type, the Fatshan[1] Chün, and a ware with opaque, rather dry glaze of *ma chün* type. But the closest copies of the mottled and splashed Chün glazes were made at Kingtehchen in the early part of the eighteenth century, the imitations being in some cases so good that were it not for the impressed Yung Chêng mark and a glimpse of the white porcelain body at the foot of the vessel, they would be distinguished with difficulty.

Chien ware takes its name from the district of Kienning,[2] in the north of the province of Fukien. It had a high reputation in the

[1] See p. 41.

[2] Mr. James M. Plumer found the kiln-sites about 30 miles due north of Kienning near Shui-chi village: see *Illustrated London News*, Oct. 26, 1935.

Sung period among tea-drinkers, the thick-glazed bowls being well suited for holding the warm tea. These bowls have a dark stoneware body and thick black glaze, which is usually streaked and mottled with golden brown or silvery markings. Sometimes they are spotted and dappled like partridge feathers, sometimes streaked with fine lines like hare's fur (fig. 44). They have always been much desired by the ceremonial tea-drinkers in Japan, where they have received the name of *temmoku*. Chinese writers say nothing of the Chien ware after the Sung dynasty; but doubtless the manufacture continued in some form in the

Figs. 44 and 45. 'Chien' ware tea-bowl. D. 4·8 in.; and 'Kian' ware bowl. Sung dynasty.

district. A small brown-glazed pot in the Collection, found in a tomb at Kienning dated 1560, is probably of local make.

A somewhat similar black glaze was used at other factories and it is frequently seen on a ware with white porcellanous body which is believed to be largely of Honan make. It was subject to many variations in the firing for which Japanese connoisseurs have invented a series of fanciful and poetic names. In general it is black variegated with golden brown; but sometimes the brown predominates, and there are specimens in which it has completely ousted the black, as on the golden brown[1] bowls found with a metal mirror in a Shensi grave.[j]

Figs. 46, 47, and 48 are examples of the black-glazed ware of Honan or Southern Chihli. A kindred ware illustrated by fig. 45 has a buff stoneware body and a thinner glaze of brown-black colour. The exterior of such bowls is usually variegated with tortoiseshell markings in golden brown, and the interior often has a light-brown hare's fur glaze in which are painted designs in black. This peculiar ware, which has very decided characteristics in its shapes and finish, is reputed to have been made at the Yung-ho kilns, near Kian, in Kiangsi; but the statement must be accepted with reserve.

[1] The Japanese call this type of ware *kaki temmoku*.

Ting ware is one of the most important and certainly one of the best known of the Sung wares. Its place of origin is Tingchow,

Figs. 46 and 47. Vase (H. 8·3 in.) and bottle from Külu: 11th century.

Fig. 48. Honan bowl. Sung. D. 3·1 in.

in the Chengting prefecture, in Chihli; and the manufacture appears to have existed in the T'ang dynasty, though it did not attain high repute until it was patronized by the Sung emperors.

Chinese writers speak of brown Ting, black Ting, and red Ting. It is possible that specimens of the brown and red varieties exist unidentified among the *kaki temmoku* wares of Honan, while such a piece as the black-glazed hemispherical bowl on three ball-feet seems to fulfil the requirements of black Ting. But at present the only kind identified with certainty is the white Ting, of which the finer varieties are known as *pai ting* (white Ting) and *fên ting* (flour Ting), while there is a coarser kind known as *t'u ting* (earthy Ting).

The finer Ting ware has a close-grained greyish white body, translucent in its thinner parts (the transmitted light having a reddish tinge) and satisfying most of the definitions of porcelain. Its glaze is a warm ivory-white, and it is apt to collect here and there in gummy drops on the exterior of bowls and dishes. These 'tear-drops' are regarded as evidence of genuineness by collectors. The bowls and dishes, of which the ware chiefly consists, generally have a glazed foot and raw mouth-rim, giving the impression of having been fired upside down. The raw edge is often concealed by a metal collar. The better specimens have designs carved or etched in the body, others are ornamented by pressing in a mould.[1] Good specimens of this ivory-white ware with bold free-hand carving are among the most beautiful works of the Sung potter.

When the Sung court fled south of the Yangtze in 1127 the manufacture of a Ting ware was carried on, probably by potters who were removed from Tingchow, in the Chi Chou district of Kiangsi, and the New Ting, or Southern Ting, made here was regarded by the Chinese in after years as practically indistinguishable from the old. The truth of both these statements is attested by a dish in Sir Percival David's collection inscribed 'made by the Shu family at Yung-ho in the Shao Hsing period' (=A.D. 1131–62).[2]

It is probable that the Ting ware was also copied at Kingtehchen at an early date. There were certainly potters there who specialized in such wares at the end of the Ming period; and the beautiful creamy white 'soft-paste' porcelains of the Manchu period are clearly descendants of the Ting yao.[3] A number of Ting bowls and dishes are shown in Bay IV, a specimen of outstanding merit being the dish (fig. 49). It was found in a Manchurian tomb, dated by internal evidence to the twelfth century, but it was unfortunately damaged in the exca-

---

[1] There are two moulds in the Collection, one for impressing Ting dishes and one for Ting or northern celadon bowls; both have incised inscriptions including Sung dates.

[2] *Shao hsing nien yung ho shu chia tsao.* Yung-ho is a village in the Chi Chou district of the Kian prefecture of Kiangsi. See Catalogue of the Chinese Exhibition, No. 1170.

[3] *yao* = kiln, or ware.

vation. It is probably a specimen of the *pai ting* of the Northern
Sung period and its beautifully carved lotus design is worthy of
the highest Sung traditions. The Collection includes plain white,
etched and moulded specimens[k], and several pieces of the *t'u ting*
type with earthy-looking body and soft, yellowish glaze minutely

FIG. 49. Ting ware dish. Sung dynasty. D. 11·8 in.

crackled or crazed (fig. 50). Doubtless many of these are Southern
Ting; and there is one interesting bowl with carved phoenix
designs in the interior which seems to be a connecting link between
the Ting ware and the true porcelain of Kingtehchen. It has the
usual Ting technique, with bare mouth-rim, and the Ting shape:
but the ware is highly porcellanous and translucent.

White wares more or less resembling the Ting types, but of
inferior reputation, were made at quite a large number of
recorded factories in the provinces of Chihli, Shansi, Anhwei,
Kiangsu, Kiangsi, and Chekiang; and it is practically impossible
to distinguish the several kinds of manufacture among the mass

of coarse wares of this class which has come from tombs and excavations in recent years. We do know, however, that a large quantity of a peculiar white ware has been dug up on the early Sung site at Küluhsien, though it does not necessarily follow that

Fig. 50.   *T'u ting* ware vase. Sung. H. 6·8 in.

it was made on the spot. It is a buff-grey stoneware with a coating of white slip and colourless glaze minutely crackled, which gave it a pleasantly soft creamy white surface.

The town of *Chü-lu*,[1] which was destroyed by inundation in A.D. 1108, lay 70 miles N. of Tzechow and 90 miles S. of Tingchow, in Southern Chihli. The buried site has been completely excavated and the pottery, which has been recovered in considerable quantity, though mostly of the ordinary domestic kind,

[1] A modern town of the same name (post-office spelling, Külu) covers part of the old site. Külu is a *hsien* or district city, as distinct from a *chou* or departmental city, and a *fu* or prefectural city.

has great interest for the student because it can be definitely dated to the early Sung period. The little group of specimens[1] in Bay IV includes the types known as Northern celadon, black-glazed Honan ware, coarse Ting wares, *ying ch'ing* and the cream-white ware just described. There is no evidence to show whether these wares were made locally, and it is quite possible that they were supplied by the great pottery centres of Tingchow and Tzechow which are situated at no great distance.

Fig. 51. Box from Kiating pagoda: about A.D. 1000. D. 4·7 in.

Again, certain vases in the Collection are labelled Kiangnan Ting. Kiangnan is an old name for the two provinces Kiangsu and Anhwei, a large district in which many manufactures of the Ting type wares were located; but the special kind represented by these vases has a buff stoneware body and a thick creamy glaze usually crackled and clouded with buff, and often with a rough ostrich-egg surface.[m] With them are a number of later wares with creamy white and generally crackled glaze of Ting type, ranging from Ming to modern times.

The white bowls of Tayi, in Szechwan, have been mentioned already among the T'ang wares, and it would not be surprising if a porcellanous ware of Ting type should have been found in that province. The little round box (fig. 51) is an interesting and important specimen, which was taken from the foundation of the Kiating pagoda. Kiating is about 75 miles S. of Tayi, and the pagoda was built about A.D. 1000.

Another and a more intriguing kind of Sung porcelain has a faintly bluish[1] or greenish white glaze over a very translucent body. It is a glassy ware, fired at a lower temperature than the normal white porcelain, and in its best examples it is singularly delicate and beautiful (fig. 52). It appears only to be known from excavated specimens and like all the burial wares it varies much in quality. It is found widely distributed, from Szechwan in the west to the tombs of Song-do in Corea, and recently it has

FIG. 52. Bowl with *ying ch'ing* glaze. Sung. D. 4·5 in.

been unearthed in considerable quantity in Kiangsi. But we have as yet no clue to its place of origin and it passes under the trade name of *ying ch'ing* (misty blue) in allusion to the tint of its glaze.

The last large Sung group consists of the pottery from *Tzechow* (Tz'ŭ Chou), in the southern corner of Chihli and not very far distant from Tingchow. The Tzechow potteries, which can be traced back to the Sui dynasty (A.D. 589–618), had a high reputation in the Sung period and continue their activities at the present day. The ware is a buff-grey stoneware. Coated with white slip and covered with translucent glaze, it would be very like some of the Ting-type wares of which the attribution is uncertain. But the typical Tzechow wares[n] are decorated— (1) with free and artistic designs painted in black slip or black and brown, or (2) with graffiato ornament; and in both cases they have a very distinctive appearance. The latter process

---

[1] The blue is due to iron, and the presence of this mineral in the body of the ware accounts for the reddening of unglazed areas such as those under the bases of vessels. See Sir Herbert Jackson's paper in *Transactions of the Oriental Ceramic Society*, 1926–7.

FIG. 53. Tzechow pillow: dated 1071. L. 8·6 in.

FIG. 54. Tzechow vase: dated 1305. H. 10 in.

admits of much variety, but two examples will explain the
general principles of it. The pillow, which can be dated to the
year 1071, has a coating of slip through which the design is
carved so as to expose the body of the ware beneath, and the
whole is glazed (fig. 53). The handsome jar (fig. 55) in the

middle of the Case has a thick brown-black glaze which has been cut away, before firing, round the edges of the design, leaving a black relief standing out on the grey body. This black glaze is akin to that discussed on p. 30 under the heading of Chien ware, and it is likely that some of the so-called Honan black wares are

FIG. 55. Tzechow vase: probably Yüan dynasty. H. 14 in.

really productions of Tzechow. The specimens in Bay IV have been assigned various dates ranging from the Sung dynasty to the nineteenth century; and with them are some blue- and green-glazed vases of a different ware but analogous decoration, which have been classed as Tzechow type, and a jar with slip designs on a pinkish brown ground which was probably made at Yo Chou, in Shensi. There were doubtless many factories in different districts making the black-glazed and black-painted stoneware.[1] Traces of a considerable industry, for instance, have

[1] Prof. Pelliot (*Notes sur l'histoire de la céramique Chinoise*, *T'oung Pao*, vol. xxii, p. 52, 1923) quotes the following from Mr. Lo Chên-yu, the Chinese antiquary:

been found near Chiaotso in Northern Honan; and the fragments and wasters obtained on the site (Bay V) include the common Tzechow types as well as coarse white porcelain and Chün wares.

Decoration in painted enamels was not fashionable in the Sung period, but there are specimens in the Collection with decoration in green, iron-red, and yellow on a body and glaze of the Tzechow type. We gather, too, from literary evidence that painting in underglaze blue was also practised; but fully authenticated examples are still to seek. A possible specimen of this rare type is a bottle with floral scrolls, which is reported to have come from a Sung tomb at Kweiki, in Kiangsi; and the form, style, and nature[1] of the ware are not inconsistent with the attribution.

The Yüan dynasty, established by the conquering Mongols under Kublai Khan, ruled the Chinese Empire from 1280 to 1368. A Tzechow vase (fig. 54) belongs to this period, and examples of Lungchüan celadon and blue and white porcelain with Yüan dates are known.[2] But the only distinctive ware⁰ associated with this period is a white porcelain with designs in moulded relief in which are concealed characters such as *shu fu* (pivot palace), &c. Otherwise for the purposes of this Handbook the Yüan dynasty may be simply regarded as an extension of the Sung.

'Porcelain pillows (*tz'ŭ chên*) come from the ancient kilns east of Yen-chia-chuang which is beyond the northern suburb of Changte. Small porcelain figures of persons (*tz'ŭ jên*), horses and dogs, not more than one inch in height, come from the kilns of the Wang family, sixty *li* west of Changte. Porcelain (*tz'ŭ*) wine jars of the Sung and Yüan period decorated in black on a white ground come from Yangcheng, in Shansi.' Changte is in the extreme north of Honan only a few miles south of Tzechow, of which it was formerly the prefectural town. The small figures made at the Wang factories are, it is added, of Sung and Yüan date. Wine jars decorated in black on a white ground would seem to be of the Tzechow type. It is known that this kind of ware was also made in other parts of China, such as Poshan, in Shantung; but at present we have not the means of distinguishing the different fabriques and it is all classed under the heading Tzechow type. Yangcheng is in the extreme south of Shansi; but in view of the fact that large numbers of the black-painted and black-glazed graffiato wares of the Tzechow type are found along the bend of the Yellow River and the borders of Mongolia, it is probable that there were several centres of manufacture farther north.

[1] A rather coarse porcelain, burnt red in the unglazed parts but with a white, sugary fracture, with a thick, bubbly, greyish white glaze. The blue is a strong dark greyish colour and the floral scrolls are admirably drawn in a style which is reflected in the early Ming blue and white porcelain. Kweiki is no great distance from Kingtehchen.

[2] See *Catalogue of Chinese Pottery and Porcelain in the Collection of Sir Percival David, Bt.*, London, 1934, Plates LI and CXXXI.

MISCELLANEOUS POTTERY

(BAYS IV and V)

THERE are and always have been numbers of obscure potteries scattered up and down the eighteen provinces of China and supplying local needs. The names of some of them are recorded,

FIG. 56. Tzechow vase. Sung. H. 14·8 in.

FIG. 57. Vase of Tzechow type. Sung. H. 15·4 in.

but the means of identifying their wares are almost entirely lacking; and the bulk of the miscellaneous Chinese pottery in our Collections must perforce remain anonymous. Three Ming types are illustrated in figs. 58–60, and of these fig. 59 comes from a tomb in Szechwan, while figs. 58 and 60, which come respectively from Borneo and Siam, are doubtless the products of a southern Chinese coastal factory.

Kwangtung Ware (BAY V)

There are, however, a few identifiable types. Canton stoneware is universally known. It comes from the large potteries which have been active for several centuries at Shekwan, by Fatshan, the great manufacturing town which lies some ten miles west of Canton. The typical Shekwan or Fatshan ware is a hard-

FIGS. 58, 59, and 60. Ming pottery jars. H. of fig. 58, 9 in.

FIG. 61. Lotus-leaf dish: Kwangtung stoneware, 17th century.
D. 8·2 in.

fired material varying from buff to reddish brown at the base and coated with a thick flocculent glaze heavily mottled and dappled with blue, grey, brown, and other combinations. Other specimens will be seen to have a rich *flambé* red; and others again with a celadon green glaze on a coarse porcellanous body which burns bright red in the exposed parts are doubtfully ascribed to Shekwan; and there is the so-called Fatshan Chün ware with thick opalescent glaze imitating the effect of the Chün Chou wares (see pp. 27 and 29). Little is known of the earlier history of the Shekwan potteries, but there is small excuse for assigning early dates to the existing specimens of their stoneware. A few may go back to the Ming dynasty, a few more to the earlier reigns of the Ch'ing; but the majority are not older than the nineteenth century and the industry is flourishing to-day.

 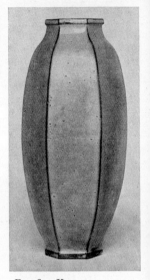

Fig. 62. Kwangtung vase. ? Ming.
H. 12·4 in.

Fig. 63. Kwangtung vase.
? Ming. H. 6·9 in.

The older potteries at Yeungkong (Yang-chiang) on the coast are only a name to us; but they may have been responsible for some of the earlier types of ware attributed by the Chinese to Kwangtung. There is, for instance, a group with buff body and a thick, opaque, paint-like glaze of grey or lavender-grey tint which remotely resembles Chün ware (fig. 62), and there is a fine-grained brown stoneware with flocculent grey glaze (fig. 63) which in China are usually attributed to Kwangtung.

Ihing and other Wares (BAY V, CASES B AND C AND TABLE-CASE)

The potteries at Ihing (Yi-hsing), west of the Great Lake in Kiangsu, date from the early years of the sixteenth century and are still active. They are noted for an admirable stoneware of various colours, red, brown, buff, drab, &c., made with judicious blends of the coloured clays found in the neighbouring hills.

The typical Ihing ware is unglazed and perfectly plain, or decorated with applied, moulded, or incised designs, the last often
in the form of calligraphic inscriptions. Much of it is tea ware;
and as it came to Europe with the importation of tea, it furnished

FIGS. 64 and 65. Ihing ware teapot, in form of a finger citron, and
spill vase, with mark of Ming-yüan. H. 4·25 in.

FIG. 66. Ihing teapot. H. 4·3 in.

models for the first European teapots, such as those made by
de Milde and others in Holland (Bay XXIII, Case F), Dwight
at Fulham, and Elers in Staffordshire (Bay XII, Cases A and B).
Incidentally the Ihing ware was classed with the American-
Indian *buccaro* on its first arrival in Europe. The collection in
Bay V (Cases B and C) comprises many varieties and illustrates
the different coloured bodies and types of decoration (figs. 64–7).
It includes a number of pieces which can be dated in the seventeenth and eighteenth centuries and one or two with post-
humous marks of Ming potters such as that of Ming-yüan. It

will be seen that some of the ware (particularly the later specimens) is painted with opaque enamels, and that a few pieces have a glazed surface. An Ihing potter named Ou, who lived at the end of the Ming period, had a wide reputation for glazed wares imitating 'Ko ware crackle and Kuan and Chün ware colours'. The tradition of Ou's glazes was preserved and Ihing Chün, like the Fatshan Chün, is one of the recognized imitations of the Sung Chün ware. A bowl in the Collection has a hard red body of Ihing type and may belong to the group under discussion; and there are other glazed specimens conjecturally assigned to Ihing and the Kwangtung potteries. Three small vases with dark brown glaze and stamped ornaments applied in relief, are believed to have been made at the Liuli-chü potteries, near Peking; and two large jars, with white slip designs and brown glaze, are probably of Soochow make.

Fig. 67. Ihing vase. H. 18·7 in.

The series of opium-pipe bowls is interesting for the great variety of pottery and porcelain included in it. Much care was lavished on these little objects which are often gems of manufacture; and their decoration will be found to include ornaments and glazes not often seen on ordinary wares.

Many of the unidentified pottery vessels and ornaments were doubtless made at tileworks, which existed in every district. Glazed pottery was and is used everywhere in China for roof-tiles and architectural ornaments, many of which are of an elaborate and highly decorative kind. Examples may be seen on the Pier-cases in Bays IV and V and under the Table-cases in Bays IV and VI. They include ancient bricks from the Great Wall of China, most of which was originally built in the third century B.C., moulded bricks of glazed pottery and porcelain from the famous Nanking

PLATE IX

Fɪɢ. 68. Statue of a Judge of Hell: pottery with coloured glazes,
late Ming. H. 54 in.

Pagoda which was completed in 1430, early Ming tiles from the Ming tombs at Nanking, yellow tiles from the Lama temple at Peking, dark blue tiles from the Temple of Heaven, and architectural ornaments from the Summer Palace, the Winter Palace, the Octagon Pavilion in Peking, and from the temple on Golden Island in the Yangtze. These wares are generally buff pottery with the usual lead-silicate glazes—green, blue, yellow, aubergine, and white; and the antefixal ornaments and roof finials are often in the form of birds, dragons, animals, and human beings modelled with much skill and spirit. Sometimes quite large statues were made in this kind of pottery, and it was not beyond the capacity of one of the better tile factories to produce such an important ceramic sculpture as the Judge of Hell (fig. 68).

KINGTEHCHEN PORCELAIN

THE MING DYNASTY

(1368–1644)

THE native Ming dynasty which ousted the Mongols in 1368 ruled at first at Nanking but moved the court to Peking in 1421. The porcelain manufacturing centre of Kingtehchen (Ching-tê Chên) is no great distance from Nanking, with which it is in communication by water; and, as it had already received Imperial orders from time to time, it was natural that the court of Nanking should look to it for supplies. According to the *Ching tê chên t'ao lu*, a factory was built in 1369 at the foot of the Jewel Hill to supply the Imperial porcelains; and in addition at least twenty private kilns were engaged on Imperial orders during the reign of Hung Wu (1368–98). It is evident that the wares supplied were regarded with favour, for the rise of Kingtehchen dates from this time and it rapidly became the centre of ceramic industry in China. Little further is heard of the old Sung factories, which seem to have died out or sunk into obscurity; and Chinese historians from this time onwards devote their attention almost exclusively to the progress made at Kingtehchen.

Coincident with this change (it is hard to say whether it was a cause or effect of it) came a revolution in porcelain decoration. The high-fired monochromes which had been the rage in the Sung period gave place to a type of decoration which had been previously regarded as inferior, viz. pictorial designs in blue or enamels. The clean white porcelain of Kingtehchen was specially adapted for this kind of embellishment, and it suited the Kingtehchen potters well to cultivate the new fashion. The lists of porcelain supplied to the later Ming Emperors comprise little else but blue and white and enamelled wares; but perhaps the change was less abrupt than it would seem to have been. It is clear, at any rate, that plain white wares were still appreciated in the early reigns, for a contemporary work (the *Ko ku yao lun*) gives the palm to white wares in the Hung Wu period (1368–98) and the best known specimens of the Yung Lo period (1403–24) are exquisitely potted white bowls of eggshell thinness and called, in fact, by the Chinese *t‘o t‘ai* or 'bodiless'.

The refinement and skill displayed in the Yung Lo bowl (fig. 73) bring home the fact that the porcelain of Kingtehchen was by no means a novelty in the Ming dynasty. There were many centuries of manufacturing tradition behind it (see p. xiii), and we need not be surprised if some of the finer and more delicate of the Ming porcelains are claimed for the earlier reigns of the dynasty.

But before discussing individual specimens it will be convenient (and it will save much repetition later on) to give a few general notes on the manufacture at Kingtehchen and the principal types of Ming porcelain.

Kingtehchen (Ching-tê Chên), a large unwalled town existing almost entirely for its ceramic industry, stands on the left bank of the Ch‘ang River which carries its goods to the Poyang Lake, and thence to the Yangtze. The surrounding district is well supplied with the materials required for porcelain manufacture, chief of which are china-clay (*kaolin*) and china-stone which the Chinese call *pai tun tzŭ* (petuntse) because it is delivered at the factories in the form of white briquettes (*tun*). Kaolin, an infusible substance, has been aptly called by the Chinese the 'bones' of the ware, while petuntse, a fusible substance, is the 'flesh'. Mingled together they make the body of the porcelain, and the petuntse (usually softened with a little lime) makes the glaze.

In the early reigns of the Ming dynasty a deposit of fine kaolin was worked in the Ma-ts‘ang hills; but this began to fail in the sixteenth century, and was practically worked out in the reign of Wan Li (1573–1619). The difficulty of replacing this fine material is reflected in the relatively inferior quality of the later Ming porcelain body. There were other clay deposits from which coarser material was obtained for the rougher and heavier wares. Petuntse was found in other localities and in varying quality: that used in the manufacture of the finer white glazes came from I-kêng.

The body of the early Ming porcelains (as may be observed at the raw edge of the bases) is of fine grain, unctuous and white;[1] and the glaze is thick and solid, sometimes with a massed appearance which the Chinese liken to mutton fat or lard. The thick

[1] It was always liable to take on a reddish tinge where exposed without protection to the fire of the kiln.

glaze has a tendency to unevenness, and elevations and depressions and even pin-holes or flaws are frequently remarked in the Ming wares. In some of the finer porcelains, obviously made for Imperial use, the glaze has a peculiar oily sheen due to an infinite number of minute depressions on the surface. This is perhaps the 'chicken skin' glaze of the Chinese texts.

Fig. 69. Fish-bowl, painted in underglaze blue and red: late Ming.
D. 22·5 in.

The finer wares, those made for the court and for the wealthy patrons, were second to none in manipulative skill and careful finish; but the factories which worked for the ordinary markets and the export trade used more summary methods, and their wares are often thick and heavy with roughly finished bases and undisguised joints and seams.

The typical Ming shapes are well represented in the Collection and need not be enumerated here; but with regard to the Ming decorations, a few comments are necessary. Ornament on the white wares is moulded in low relief, painted in white slip, carved, or etched with a needle point. In each case it is covered over with glaze; and this unobtrusive decoration is called by the Chinese *an hua* or secret ornament. In some cases the white porcelain is decorated with high reliefs which have been separately modelled and stuck on with liquid clay. The reliefs are sometimes unglazed, in which case it was a common practice to cover them with oil-gilding. The coloured wares are mostly painted with pictorial and formal designs in blue or enamel colours, or decorated with raised, carved, or incised designs filled in with coloured glazes. A few are painted in underglaze red and a few others have monochrome glazes of various colours. By far the largest group is the 'blue and white', i.e. that decorated in blue on a white ground, and occasionally with white designs reserved in a blue ground. The blue colour is derived from cobaltiferous ore of manganese which was either obtained locally or imported from abroad. The local blue was inclined to be dull and greyish in tone, and the best Ming blues are those imported (apparently from Persia) and known by the name of Mohammedan blue. This imported blue was costly and the supply uncertain, and as a rule it was reserved for the Imperial factories. It was available in the Hsüan Tê period (1426–35) and consequently the blue and white of that time had a high reputation: subsequently the supply seems to have failed until the reigns of Chêng Tê and Chia Ching in the sixteenth century. The Mohammedan blue was not used by itself, but blended with native mineral in proportions which varied according to the quality of the ware.

The blue designs were painted with a brush on the raw body of the ware; the glaze was then applied and one firing sufficed to bake body and glaze and develop the colour of the decoration. The typical Ming blue and white is painted with clearly defined outlines, the designs being filled in with flat washes of blue: but there is another style in which the designs are carefully pencilled throughout, no washes being used. The lists of porcelains supplied to the Palace in the middle of the sixteenth century give a great number of designs used on the Ming blue and white. Many of them were derived from well-known pictures, illustrations of romance, &c., and even from designs specially painted by the court artists: still more (and these include the more intricate patterns) from coloured silk brocades, &c. Doubtless the stock designs were collected and preserved in pattern-books. They were certainly repeated frequently and retained their popularity long after the fall of the Ming dynasty.

Another underglaze colour was the red derived from copper which was occasionally used for painted designs similar to those in underglaze blue. This red was evidently a difficult colour to control; but it was used with conspicuous success in the two classic reigns of the fifteenth century, Hsüan Tê and Ch'êng Hua, not only for painted designs but as a monochrome glaze colour. It is variously described as *hsien hung* (fresh or vivid red), *pao shih hung* (the red of precious stones) and *chi hung* which means 'massed red', 'sky-clearing red', or 'sacrificial red' according to the character which is used to represent *chi*.

In later reigns much difficulty was experienced in producing this red colour, and the red enamel derived from iron (*fan hung*) was often used in its place. But the copper-red was not wholly abandoned, for we find it occasionally on Chêng Tê and Wan Li porcelains either alone or in company with underglaze blue.

Ming porcelains decorated in colours fall into two general groups known by the Chinese names *san ts'ai* and *wu ts'ai*, three- and five-colour wares. The term 'three-colour' is reserved for those noble porcelains of which the designs are outlined in threads of clay (cloisonné fashion), incised, carved or pierced, and washed in with coloured glazes. The glazes are of the lead-silicate kind and do not require the full heat of the porcelain kiln to develop them. Consequently this kind of porcelain is 'biscuited', i.e. the body of the ware is fired first in the full heat, and the glazes are subsequently applied and fired in the cooler parts of the porcelain kiln. They are in fact 'medium-fired', or to use the French definition, glazes *de demi-grand feu*. The usual colours are green, yellow, aubergine, dark violet blue, turquoise, and a colourless glaze which does duty for white. They are derived respectively from copper, antimony or iron, manganese, cobalt, and again copper; they are usually applied in combinations of two or three with another as background, the precise number three (implied in *san ts'ai*) not being too rigidly observed. The early medium-fired glazes are of considerable hardness and often cloudy and rather opaque; but on some sixteenth-century ware (on porcelain, for instance, of the Chêng Tê period) we find similarly coloured glazes of a more even, transparent, and softer-looking nature. For the sake of distinction these may be described as 'softer lead-silicate glazes'.

The term *wu ts'ai* (five colour) is applied by the Chinese to decoration in vitrifiable enamels. It is an elastic term, not restricted to cases in which exactly five colours are used, but applied to polychrome enamelled wares in general. The enamels, like the glazes, are glasses, but, containing more lead, they are therefore more fusible. They are tinted with mineral oxides and fused on to the ware at a comparatively low temperature in a muffle-kiln or stove. Much the same materials are used as in the glazes, and a similar range of colour results: but the enamels are more manageable than the glazes and better suited for intricate brushwork. The Ming palette comprises greens of several shades, yellow (often a cloudy, amber colour), aubergine or purplish

E

brown, a turquoise green (peculiar to Ming porcelain and replaced later by a violet blue enamel),[1] a thin, but rather opaque and often iridescent tomato red (derived from iron), and a dry reddish brown pigment which is used for drawing outlines and, covered with transparent green, to form a composite black

Fig. 70.   Garden seat: 'three-colour' porcelain, 15th century.
H. 14·3 in.

enamel. These enamels can be applied direct to the unglazed body, or 'biscuit', in which case their appearance does not greatly differ from that of the softer *san ts'ai* glazes. This on-biscuit enamelling was certainly employed on Ming porcelain, but it was used to a far greater extent on the porcelain of the succeeding dynasty. But the more usual application of the enamels was in designs painted on the glazed porcelain. In one large group of the five-colour porcelain the on-glaze enamels are combined with underglaze blue. Decoration of this kind was

[1] Exceptional and anticipatory use of this blue enamel in the Wan Li period is seen on a large oblong box from the Eumorfopoulos Collection.

used from the early reigns of the Ming dynasty onwards, but it was specially favoured in the later periods and, indeed, it is generally known as *wan li wu ts'ai* (polychrome of the Wan Li period). In another group, red and green (especially the former) are particularly prominent, and this is often called the 'red and green family' (fig. 71). In another, in which all the enamels are employed impartially (fig. 72), attention is drawn to the tur-

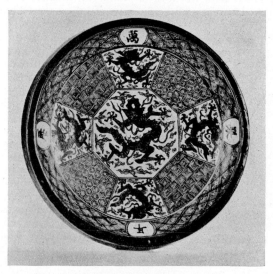

FIG. 71. Stand: 'red and green' family, Wan Li mark. D. 7·5 in.

quoise green as a sure sign of Ming workmanship. Gilding was used on Ming porcelain at all periods, often applied in the form of leaf-gold. It should be noted that the Ming enamelled wares were closely studied by the Japanese potters, who copied them with great exactitude.

Ming monochromes are relatively uncommon, but they include a wide range of colours. Among the high-fired glazes are white and the cream-white imitations of Ting ware; a lustrous black, with brown reflections something between the *temmoku* glaze[1] and the K'ang Hsi mirror-black; celadon green; copper-red, and a few *flambé* glazes which are probably accidental effects; a variety of cobalt blues; and grey crackles of the Ko type. Of the medium-fired glazes we find green, yellow, aubergine, and turquoise used as single colours; and several of the enamels were similarly employed, notably green and iron-red. The so-called

[1] See p. 30.

'apple-green' is a composite colour formed by a wash of transparent emerald green over a grey crackle.

Other of the less common kinds of Ming decoration are openwork, biscuit reliefs, slip-painting, and lacquering. Openwork (*ling lung*) is seen in its simpler forms on the reticulated vases, jars, and barrel-shaped seats of fifteenth-century date; but the *chefs d'œuvre* of this process are the small bowls with sides and covers pierced with fretwork of wonderful fineness which were made in the last reigns of the dynasty. To these the Chinese gave the name of *kuei kung*, or devil's work. Occasionally the fret designs are deeply incised without being actually cut out in openwork. Openwork medallions are sometimes left without glaze, and these biscuit ornaments were often covered with gilding applied over a red medium. Similar gilding is found on the small relief ornaments (figures and the like) in biscuit which were sometimes applied to the sides of bowls and vases. Again, patterns and even pictorial designs in very low relief were made by painting in slip (i.e. liquid clay) or by working up shavings and strips of porcelain clay with a wet brush. These were sometimes covered with the glaze; but more often they stand out from a background of blue, brown, or celadon glaze. A rare vase (fig. 104) illustrates the use of lacquer on porcelain, a freakish and unnatural combination not often found on Ming wares.

FIG. 72. Ink screen: 16th century, enamelled porcelain. H. 6 in.

Having learnt the essential features of the Ming technique we can now take a rapid chronological survey of the Collection, which is exhibited in Bay XXXII, Cases D, E, F and Standard-case, in Bay XXXI, Case C and part of the Table-case, and in the north end of Standard-case E.

Hung Wu (1368–98). There is no specimen in the Collection which can be assigned with certainty to the first reign of the Ming dynasty. If we could trust the reign-marks on Chinese porcelain, a dish in Standard-case E, south side, belongs to the Hung Wu period. But it should be said at once that the reign-marks cannot be accepted without strong collateral evidence, and in this case the type of decoration in the border—in white reserved in a blue ground—is far more sophisticated than one would expect at this early period. There is good reason to suppose that painting in blue was practised by the Sung and Yüan potters, though it was not in favour before the Ming dynasty; and the earliest Ming blue and whites have a certain tradition behind them. A few saucers are known with spirited figure-drawing, which have the Hung Wu mark; and it is possible that a small bowl in the Collection, decorated with children at play, belongs to this time.[p] The *Ko ku yao lun* praises the white Hung Wu porcelain of which the glaze was 'thick and lustrous like massed lard': and among the white wares in the Collection is a bowl with thick, uneven glaze of lard-like appearance, which is clearly of early date and may possibly be a Hung Wu specimen. The interior has been engraved with Arabic inscriptions, probably in Persia.

Yung Lo (1403–24). The most celebrated wares of this period were the white cups with broad rim and small foot suited for holding in the palm of the hand (*ya shou pei*, or press-hand cups), and of an eggshell thinness which is graphically expressed by the Chinese phrase *t'o t'ai*, or bodiless. A specimen of this ware (fig. 73) is now quite famous. It is a wide-mouthed conical bowl with a faint design of two Imperial five-clawed dragons admirably drawn in white slip under the glaze and visible, like a water-mark in paper, when held against the light (fig. 74). On the bottom inside is the mark of the period in archaic characters traced with a needle point. The walls of this bowl taper upwards to an incredible thinness, until at the top they appear to be really bodiless, and to consist of glaze alone. The finish of the piece is fine without being meticulous, the outline of the sides is pleasantly undulating, and the glaze, which is thick, is not without an occasional pinhole or flaw, such as are proverbially characteristic of the early Ming wares. This bowl was doubtless made at the Imperial factory. Elsewhere there are two 'press-hand cups' of an inferior white porcelain,[q] which may be the work of a private factory of the same period. Their decoration is moulded in faint relief. There is also a bowl[r] of coarse blue and white porcelain with figures in a boat and a poem by Su Shih outside, and the Yung Lo mark inside. It appears to be Ming ware and may possibly be a rough specimen of the period. A small bowl, one of a pair, has a slight blue design inside and the exterior coated with an opaque tomato-red on which are scrolls and flowers in gold. On the base, which is slightly conical, is the mark of the Yung Lo period. The pair to this bowl is shown in company with three others with similar decoration.[1] On two of these the red is more orange-coloured and translucent; and in the third it is duller and more iridescent and the bottom is slightly convex inside. It is probable that this is a Yung Lo type, which was revived in the sixteenth century at the time

[1] Postcard series, C 12, No. 173.

when difficulties were experienced in making the underglaze copper-red and the iron-red (*fan hung*) was used in its place.

Hsüan Tê (1426–35). The porcelain of this reign has a very high reputation. Supplies of Mohammedan blue were available and the Imperial blue and white was of exceptionally high quality. The underglaze copper-red (*chi hung*) was at its best at this time and various kinds of polychrome porcelains are men-

FIG. 75. Blue and white ewer: 15th century.
H. 11·5 in.

tioned among the successes of this reign. The finer specimens of Hsüan Tê porcelain are exceedingly rare to-day, but there are a few pieces in the Collection (probably the work of private factories) which can reasonably claim to be of this date. Among the blue and white there are four or five specimens attributed to the fifteenth century on grounds of style. Of these, two ewers bear the Hsüan Tê mark, and another has an exceptionally well-drawn design in a rather mottled blue which is apparently a Hsüan Tê type. The mottled blue is further illustrated by a ewer (fig. 75) and two bowls which have the Hsüan Tê mark. The little flask reputed on somewhat doubtful evidence to have belonged to the famous sixteenth-century collector Hsiang Yüan-pien, is an interesting but uncertain specimen. A saucer-dish[1]

[1] Postcard series, C 12, No. 167.

PLATE X

Fɪɢ. 73. White 'eggshell' porcelain bowl: Yung Lo period

Fɪɢ. 74. Interior of the same with drawing of the design. D. 8·7 in.

with a remarkable red glaze is in all probability an example of the rare *chi hung*.[s] A probable specimen of five-colour porcelain of the period is seen in a square box with Japanese bronze lid; it combines underglaze blue with enamels painted on the glaze and has the Hsüan Tê mark. The same description applies to an elegant cup (fig. 76) in the form of a lotus leaf from the Eumorfopoulos Collection. Though no marked examples of three-colour ware of this reign are known, it cannot be doubted that they were made. The *Po wu yao lan*, one of the best-known Chinese commentaries on Ming wares, mentions among the Hsüan Tê porcelains 'the beautiful barrel-shaped

FIG. 76. Cup with Hsüan Tê mark. L. 5·75 in.

seats, some with openwork ground, the designs filled in with colours, gorgeous as cloud brocades, others with solid ground filled in with colours in engraved floral designs, so beautiful and brilliant as to dazzle the eye'; and this description applies so closely to such pieces as the barrel-shaped garden seat, wine-jar, and reticulated vase in the Standard-case in Bay XXXII, that we cannot fail to see in it the well-known three-colour types. Figs. 70, 79, 80 illustrate the carved, pierced, incised, and cloisonné kinds of decoration and the typical *san ts'ai* colours in the two most usual backgrounds of turquoise and dark violet blue. It is not claimed that these pieces are of the Hsüan Tê period, though several of them are doubtless of fifteenth-century date; but this type, perhaps the most decorative of all the Ming productions, was made continuously for at least two hundred years and it is hardly possible to identify the work of any one reign.

It should be added here that the *san ts'ai* glazes were used on pottery and stoneware as well as porcelain, at the numerous potworks scattered throughout China. The lovely vase in the same Case, with chrysanthemum designs in relief in a peacock-blue ground, is a good example of their use on a porcellanous stoneware base (fig. 77). Such wares were not made at King-tehchen, and, though they form a fairly large and well-defined group, we are still ignorant of their place of origin: nor does this particular type appear to be older than the sixteenth century.

A dish of somewhat unusual form in Bay XXXI, with lotus

FIG. 77. Vase of 'three-colour' stone-ware. 16th century. H. 18 in.

FIG. 78. Bottle of 'three-colour' stone-ware: Late Ming. H. 10·75 in.

scrolls in gold and the Hsüan Tê mark in blue, is doubtless a Hsüan Tê type if not actually of the period.[t]

Ch'êng Hua (1465–87). Chinese writers are silent on the porce-lains of the thirty years following the reign of Hsüan Tê and we have no means of identifying them. But the reign of Ch'êng Hua ranks with that of Hsüan Tê as one of the classic periods of the art at Kingtehchen; and potters of subsequent periods pay impartial tributes to both by copying their reign-marks promis-cuously. The supply of Mohammedan blue appears to have failed at this time; but much stress is laid on the delicacy and beauty of the Ch'êng Hua enamelled wares, and we gather that underglaze red was used with marked success. There are many

PLATE XI

FIGS. 79 and 80. 'Three-colour' porcelain; 15th century. Vase with openwork; and wine jar with decoration in 'cloisonné' style. H. 13 in.

specimens with the Ch'êng Hua mark in the Collection, but few which have any serious claim to belong to the period. A small rice-bowl painted with figures of Tung-fang So with his peach in clear silvery blue (fig. 81) and a stem-cup[1] with pencilled designs of animals and symbols on a wave pattern are likely specimens of Ch'êng Hua blue and white: and in the Standard-case, Bay XXXII, is a large vase (fig. 82) with stiff floral scrolls in enamel colours and underglaze blue in a ground of grey crackle. This last vase is of massive build, one of the heavier types of Ming porcelain which have been able to survive to our day, though not without damage. There are several other

FIG. 81. Blue and white bowl with Ch'êng Hua mark. D. 4·2 in.

known specimens of this type bearing, like this one, the Ch'êng Hua mark in a sunk panel under the base, and all more or less truncated.

Hung Chih (1488–1505). From the few allusions to Hung Chih porcelain we gather that the yellow-glazed specimens were best known; and for the rest we can only infer that the traditions of the celebrated reigns which preceded were kept alive. The marked specimens in the Collection include a baluster vase (fig. 83) with incised dragon designs enamelled green, a saucer dish, and a bowl in Bay XXXI. The dish and bowl are white porcelain of high quality; and on the former two distinct glazes are observable, a finer one on the interior and sides and a more ordinary glaze under the base.

Chêng Tê (1506–21). Supplies of Mohammedan blue were again forthcoming in this reign. It was apparently of dark tone and rivalled the Hsüan Tê colour; and some of it, we are told, found its way to the private manufacturers. There are several specimens of Chêng Tê blue and white in Bay XXXII, including an interesting series of objects decorated with 'Mohammedan

[1] A somewhat similar cup in Bay XXXII, formerly in the Leverton Harris Collection, has a European silver mount of about the year 1530.

FIG. 83. Vase with Hung Chih mark. H. 14·1 in.

FIG. 82. Vase painted in blue and enamels; Ch'êng Hua mark. H. 16·3 in.

FIG. 84. Ink-pallet: Chêng Tê blue and white. L. 9·8 in.

scrolls' of lotus pattern and medallions with Arabic inscriptions (fig. 84). Probably made for Mohammedans in China, these pieces are stoutly built but of a fine white ware, and the blue though rendered misty by the thick bubbly glaze is of fine tone. A thinner and more highly finished specimen (probably an Imperial piece) is the saucer-dish with a well-executed design of five-clawed dragons among lotus scrolls in a delicate greyish blue (fig. 85). Underglaze red was used in the decoration of Chêng Tê

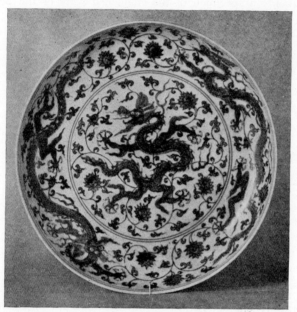

Fig. 85. Saucer-dish with Imperial dragons. Chêng Tê
blue and white. D. 9·4 in.

porcelain. It is usually of a pale maroon tint, as on the dish from the Bloxam Collection. A few marked specimens in Bay **XXXI** illustrate a type of polychrome which seems to have been in favour in the Chêng Tê period, viz. that with neatly incised designs filled in with washes of the softer lead-silicate glazes (see p. 49) and sometimes enamels, green in a yellow ground[1] being a frequent combination. The glaze on these specimens often has the 'chicken skin' texture mentioned on p. 47. This class of ware was carefully copied in the Yung Chêng period (*q.v.*) and it will always be difficult to distinguish the originals from the

[1] Similar yellow glaze is used in monochrome as on a small yellow vase which may be of the Chêng Tê period.

reproductions. The characteristic Chêng Tê 'three-colour' ware has incised designs filled with washes of lead-silicate glazes which are thinner and more translucent than those of the fifteenth-century *san ts'ai*. Fig. 86 illustrates a marked specimen from the Eumorfopoulos Collection. The square scrap-bowl decorated with underglaze blue full-face dragons in a ground of yellow enamel represents another type; and the pipe-shaped bottle with enamels of the red and green family, though unmarked, is probably a specimen of the enamelled ware of the period.

FIG. 86. Flower-pot. Chêng Tê period. H. 5·7 in.

The much-browned paste visible on the base of this specimen is certainly characteristic of some known types of Chêng Tê ware.

Chia Ching (1522–66). We are told that the fine kaolin deposits at Ma-ts'ang were seriously depleted by this time, and also that the Imperial potters confessed their inability to make the underglaze copper-red and appealed for permission to use the red enamel instead. But in spite of these drawbacks the Chia Ching porcelain had a high reputation. Supplies of Mohammedan blue were again forthcoming; and the wide range of the Chia Ching blue and white can be realized even in this one Collection. The powerful dark violet blue, which is the Mohammedan blue of the period, is seen on a hexagonal bottle and a finely painted colour-stand (fig. 87). The same blue, in less pure quality, appears on two ewers, one of which has the design of a kylin lying in front of a very European-looking fountain. Both these pieces have the 'hare' mark which seems to belong to this period.

The poorer native blue, with its greyish tone, occurs on other pieces, notably a double-gourd vase in Standard-case E; and again there is an attractive little series (a ewer, kettle, bowls, and dishes) in Bay XXXII of thin crisp porcelain painted in a pale silvery blue. Specimens of this type, evidently a favourite with the foreign traders, can be traced to the latter years of the Chia Ching period; but it persisted for about a century and it will as a rule be regarded as Wan Li or later.

Fig. 87. Stand painted in Mohammedan blue. Chia Ching period.
D. 4·8 in.

Chia Ching polychromes are very varied and several of the known types are represented in the Collection. There are a few examples of the red and green family of enamels, notably the square box from the Eumorfopoulos Collection (fig. 88); and there is a saucer with broad areas of the typical iridescent Ming red; and a jar with figure subjects in underglaze blue and enamels and the 'hare' mark is an example of the typical 'five-colour' ware (fig. 92). It is an early example of a style of painting which continued through the late Ming and transition periods, and which appears again in a pair of transition beakers in Standard-case F. An interesting series of bowls in Bay XXXI belongs in part at least to this reign. The shallow wine-cup,[1] a typical Chia Ching form, has designs in the Chia Ching Mohammedan blue as well as a broad band of emerald-green enamel on which are gilt floral scrolls. The same green and gold deco-

[1] Postcard series, C 12, No. 174.

Fig. 88. Box: 'red and green' family. 16th century. L. 5·45 in.

Fig. 89. Chia Ching bowl with green and gold decoration.
D. 4·8 in.

ration on a rounded bowl¹ (with the bottom slightly convex inside) doubtless belongs to the same period (fig. 89); and similarity of form suggests the same attribution for some of the red and gold bowls in the same compartment. The red of these pieces is the iron-red enamel (*fan hung*) which was substituted for the more difficult copper-red: but we have seen that this iron-red was also used in the Yung Lo period. Another bowl of the same form with convex bottom is white with 'secret decoration' (*an hua*) traced in white slip inside, while on the exterior

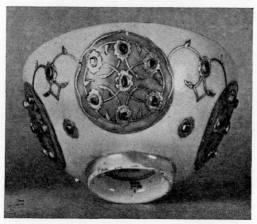

Fɪɢ. 90.   Jewelled bowl: probably Chia Ching period.
D. 4·7 in.

are four medallions outlined in red and filled in with turquoise blue, once gilt (fig. 90). This rare piece has been mounted in India or Persia with gold filigree work set with cabochon jewels. The shape of these bowls with their rounded sides and convex bottoms (doubtless the *man hsin* or 'loaf-shaped centre' of the old Chinese descriptions) seems to be characteristic of the middle Ming period. The marks on them are not usually date-marks which could indicate a definite reign, but marks of commendation (such as *fu kuei chia ch'i*—beautiful vessel for the rich and honourable), good wishes, &c. A double-gourd vase from the Bloxam Collection, with lotus scrolls in red in a green ground, and a jar (fig. 91), given by Mr. Harvey Hadden, with yellow dragon design, in a red ground, show two combinations of enamel colours much favoured in this period. Enamel decoration on the biscuit is

¹ A similar bowl with a silver-gilt mount of mid-sixteenth century date is exhibited in the Franks Room at the west end of the Gallery: and with it is a blue and white Ming bowl with European mount of the year 1580,

illustrated by a fine wide-mouthed bowl, with lotus scrolls and storks in a yellow ground (fig. 94).

The use of lead-silicate glazes as monochromes is seen in two bowls, yellow and aubergine, in Bay XXXI. The fine 'apple-green' vase has a Ming form and may belong to this period. But the most characteristic Chia Ching monochrome is the deep

Fig. 91. Vase decorated in red and yellow. Chia Ching period. H. 8·6 in.

blue glaze seen over engraved designs on a covered jar. This blue is rather purplish in tone and it is usually strewn with small points of colour as though it had been blown on in a spray. It is, however, distinct from the K'ang Hsi powder-blue (see p. 86).

Lung Ch'ing (1567–72). The ware of this reign doubtless continued the Chia Ching traditions; and it has probably been included among the specimens of that and the succeeding period, except in the rare cases in which the reign-mark has enabled us to differentiate it. An oblong box in Bay XXXII gives a good

FIGS. 92 and 93. Vase with 'five-colour' decoration: 'hare' mark; and covered vase with 'wave and plum-blossom' design. H. 15·2 in.

FIG. 94. Chia Ching bowl: enamelled on the biscuit. D. 6·9 in.

F

idea of the Lung Ch'ing blue and white (fig. 95), the blue in this case being of dark Chia Ching type. Other known specimens with the mark of the period include five-colour porcelains of good quality: but they are not represented in the Collection.

Wan Li (1573–1619). The porcelains which represent this long reign vary considerably in style and quality. There is no doubt that the Kingtehchen potters were now capable of mastering the most difficult ceramic problems. On the other hand, the finer materials used during the earlier reigns were now scarce and often not available. Add to this the fact that much of the Wan Li

FIG. 95. Box of Lung Ch'ing blue and white. L. 11·8 in.

ware in our collections belongs to the inferior class of export ware, and the great range of quality is explained. Some of the pure white bowls and dishes of the period are worthy successors of the Yung Lo bowls, and there are blue and white specimens of refined make with a blue that can hardly be distinguished from the Chia Ching Mohammedan blue. A pair of saucer-dishes, decorated in dark blue with a favourite Ming design, 'fish and waterweeds', are evidence of this; while, on the other hand, the large square beaker in Standard-case E, though clearly an Imperial piece, is of rather coarse material and is painted with a dull greyish blue (fig. 102).

The series of crisply potted porcelains with pale silvery blue designs in Bay XXXII (see p. 61) is largely of Wan Li date (figs. 96, 97); and among the miscellaneous blue and whites here and in Standard-case E are dishes of heavier build but decorated in a kindred style and doubtless intended for the same Near Eastern markets. A dish with kylin and palm tree in this Case has the hall-mark *yü t'ang chia ch'i* (beautiful vessel of the Jade Hall) which occurs on several types of late Ming porcelain, e.g. two shallow bowls in Bay XXXII with designs in underglaze

FIGS. 96 and 97. Late Ming blue and white ewer (H. 7 in.) and dish
with stork mark. D. 8·2 in.

blue[1] and underglaze red, a vase with white slip ornament on a coffee-brown ground in Bay XXXI, a dish with underglaze blue and enamels, and one of the *ling lung* bowls[2] (fig. 101).

The Wan Li polychromes include a rare beaker with figure designs, &c., in aubergine in a yellow ground, the colours applied direct to the biscuit:[3] a rare bowl (fig. 98) from the Bloxam Collection with yellow dragons in an aubergine ground: a covered jar (fig. 93) with plum blossom, symbols, &c., on an aubergine

Fig. 98. Bowl with aubergine ground. Wan Li period. D. 5·9 in.

wave pattern, which is painted on the glaze though in the style of the on-biscuit enamel work: an Imperial vase of square beaker shape with lion-mask handles and dragon and phoenix designs in underglaze blue and enamels, the typical *wan li wu ts'ai*, in Bay XXXII: a ewer[4] and box in Bay XXXI, two admirable specimens of the same type (fig. 99): and a circular stand and saucer-dish with enamels of the red and green family (fig. 71). But the most important members of this group are the two pricket candlesticks and the beaker from an Imperial altar set (fig. 100), which bear the Wan Li mark beautifully written along their lips. They are decorated with five-clawed dragons in coloured glazes in a yellow ground.

---

[1] The blue on these pieces has a powdery appearance, as though they were early examples of powder-blue: but it was probably applied with a sponge and not a blowing tube (see p. 86).   [2] See p. 52.
[3] Postcard series, C 12, No. 176.   [4] Ibid., C 12, No. 177.

PLATE XII

大明萬曆年製

Fig. 100. Flower vase from an altar set. Wan Li period.
H. 29·1 in.

Two bowls, one with cover,[1] illustrate the finer *ling lung* fretwork combined with reliefs (*tui t'o*) in biscuit and traceries in white slip. One of them has subsidiary ornament in a greyish underglaze blue (fig. 101). These are striking examples of the manipulative skill of the late Ming potters. A similar kind of fretwork, deeply cut but not perforated, is seen on the large and small bowls in Bay XXXII; the sunk parts of the pattern are

FIG. 99. Box of Wan Li 'five-colour' porcelain. D. 5·5 in.

in unglazed biscuit. Relief ornament in biscuit is further illustrated by two bottles in Bay XXXI, with a design of dragons pursuing pearls. In the same Bay is a group of porcelains effectively decorated with white slip designs on coloured backgrounds—blue, pea-green celadon (fig. 103), and coffee-brown. They are of various dates but chiefly late Ming. Near them is shown a rare specimen of Wan Li porcelain encrusted with designs in lacquer (fig. 104). It is clearly an Imperial piece and compares closely in shape, material, mark, and design of ornament with the Imperial beaker (fig. 102).

T'ien Ch'i (1621–7). The few marked specimens of T'ien Ch'i porcelain in the Collection are of coarse and inferior workmanship. They include a large blue and white bowl with dragon design and a barrel-shaped fire-vase with floral scrolls; and a

[1] Postcard series, C 12, No. 178.

FIG. 101. 'Ling lung' bowl: late Ming. D. 4·7 in.

FIG. 102. Blue and white beaker: Wan Li Imperial porcelain. H. 22 in.

FIG. 103. Bottle with design in slip: about 1500. H. 10·7 in.

saucer-dish (in Bay **XXXI**) with incised dragon design and soft lead-silicate glazes of green, aubergine, and yellow colour.

With this last are a dish with 'egg and spinach' decoration which consists of a motley of the same three colours in large patches, and two saucer-dishes with incised floral sprays filled

FIG. 104. Wan Li vase with lacquered ornament. H. 13·5 in.

in with similar coloured glazes.[u] These dishes are obviously related to the bowls with incised floral sprays in coloured grounds—yellow, green, aubergine (*brinjal*) and white—and undecipherable seal marks of the kind known as 'shop marks' in blue, some of which are of late Ming date, while others were certainly made in the Ch'ing dynasty.

Ch'ung Chêng (1628–43). A cup of rather coarse ware painted with rice-plants and geese in greyish blue has the mark of this undistinguished period which is otherwise practically unknown to porcelain collectors.

It was only natural that during the convulsions which preceded and accompanied the overthrow of the Ming and the establishment of the Manchu dynasty the peaceful industries should be neglected; and Chinese ceramic histories are virtually silent on the period between Wan Li and K'ang Hsi, viz. 1620–62. It may be that the Imperial factory was neglected during these

FIG. 105. Bottle: 'transition' blue and white: about 1640. H. 12 in.

troubled times. At any rate there was no progress to record, and we are left to find out for ourselves the characteristics of the ware of this intermediate period.

It was, however, a time when European traders were flocking to China and most of the enterprising nations of Europe had their East India companies established: and it is probable that the private factories at Kingtehchen made up in foreign orders a good deal of what they lost in an unsettled home market. European designs and even European shapes began to be adopted; and we still find occasional jugs and tankards in Chinese blue and white, but of purely European form, with Dutch or German silver mounts which can be dated to this period.

From these we gather that a rather bright violet blue and a mannered style of decoration, the recurrence of certain border patterns, e.g. that containing a formal tulip-like flower, and certain other details are typical of the transition blue and white. From this again we are enabled to recognize the transition enamelled ware and other types. Two tankards in Bay XXX and four bottle-shaped vases (fig. 105) in Standard-case E may be taken as representative specimens of the first, and a pair of tall and characteristically shaped beakers in Standard-case F of the second. Besides these, many of the coarser blue and whites and polychromes in Ming style in our Collections doubtless belong to the export goods made at this time. A few pieces, distributed through Bay XXXI and labelled seventeenth century, probably should be assigned to this period of transition.

THE CH'ING DYNASTY

(1644–1912)

THE Manchu dynasty which took the name of *Ch'ing* (pure) was established in 1644, but the process of settling the eighteen provinces of China must have monopolized the energies of the new rulers for a considerable time; and little attention was paid to such minor matters as the porcelain factories at Kingtehchen during the reign of the first Emperor, Shun Chih (1644–61). Marked specimens of this period are extremely rare and we may safely assume that the output consisted of porcelains of the late Ming and transition types.

But the Manchu emperors once firmly established proved to be enlightened patrons of the arts and industries. The Emperor K'ang Hsi succeeded to the throne in 1662 at the tender age of nine, and there is no reason to suppose that any great improvements took place at Kingtehchen during the early years of his reign. Indeed any progress, that may have been made, suffered a rude set-back in the destruction of the Imperial factory during the formidable rebellion of Wu San-kuei between 1673 and 1681. This troubled period, however, was followed by a veritable renaissance of the arts in which the Emperor himself took a great personal interest. In 1680 workshops for no less than twenty-seven different handicrafts were established in the palace precincts at Peking under the supervision of the Board of Works; and in the same year an official of the Imperial household was sent to reside at the Imperial factory at Kingtehchen which was now rebuilt. Chinese writers tell us that the conditions of the industry were vastly improved, oppression and exactions were stopped, and the workers were well cared for and contented.

The result was that no pains were spared to improve the manufacture of the ware and one of the great periods of Chinese ceramic history began.

During this classic period which embraces the greater part of three reigns, of K'ang Hsi (1662–1722), Yung Chêng (1723–35), and Ch'ien Lung (1736–95), the Imperial factory was supervised by three highly competent men—Ts'ang Ying-hsüan (appointed in 1682), Nien Hsi-yao (appointed about 1723) and T'ang Ying (1736–49); and there is no doubt that they were largely responsible for the sustained excellence of the porcelain made during these years. The debt to them is at any rate acknowledged by Chinese writers who distinguish the wares of their respective periods as Ts'ang yao, Nien yao, and T'ang yao.

The actual processes used by the Ch'ing potters are essentially the same as those employed in the Ming dynasty. They were, of course, developed and in some ways improved, and a few new glazes and colours were added; but there is little that was entirely new in the material side of the manufacture, and the few novelties in technique can be most appropriately discussed in connexion with the actual specimens. The student will notice, however, those slight but important differences in the shapes of bowls, dishes, vases, &c., and the many modifications of the standard designs which give a distinctive character to Ch'ing wares.

Trade with Europe was now established on an extensive scale and the East India companies of Spain, Portugal, Holland, England, France, Denmark, and Sweden were represented at Canton and elsewhere. The potteries of Kingtehchen were flooded with orders transmitted from the foreign merchants who demanded particular forms, not always easy to execute, and special kinds of decoration for which they actually supplied designs. In this way European influences insinuated themselves into the Chinese porcelain decoration, until towards the end of the eighteenth century the decoration of the export ware at any rate was definitely hybrid in character.

The Europeanization of the designs is hardly noticeable in the porcelains of the K'ang Hsi period, and the export ware of that time, often porcelain of very high quality, is decorated with Chinese patterns, though these are frequently crowded, confused, and meaningless in contrast with the designs on pure native wares which always convey a clear-cut meaning to the Chinese mind. Further, it is evident that the European importers delighted in bizarre and grotesque forms and there is no doubt that the Chinese manufacturers pandered to this taste. This will explain the many K'ang Hsi vases with needlessly complicated outlines which figure in Western collections. Neither they nor the confused decoration which covers them should be regarded

PLATE XIII

Figs. 106, 107, and 108. Two vases and a dish (D. 11 in.), K'ang Hsi *famille verte*

as true types of K'ang Hsi porcelain, although they often have considerable decorative value thanks to their attractive material and brilliant colouring.

The Western influences in these cases were imposed on the Chinese potters by the conditions of trade; but there is a group of choice porcelains which display a deliberately adopted Western character. This is the so-called Ku-yüeh-hsüan porcelain, some of which even includes European figure subjects in its decoration. The school of painting established by Imperial order in Peking by Castiglione (Lang Shih-ning) was probably responsible for the foreign elements in this group, which belong to the reigns of Yung Chêng and Ch'ien Lung and to which we shall return later (p. 99).

In general, the K'ang Hsi porcelains are distinguished by fine flowing lines and excellence of potting, and by decoration which has a boldness and breadth worthy of the best Ming traditions. As time went on a tendency to over-refinement manifested itself, and much of the Ch'ien Lung ware, though cleverly made and often a perfect marvel of manipulative skill, is effeminate and finicking in decoration.

K'ANG HSI

(1662–1722)

It was not always possible in arranging the pier-cases of the Ceramic Gallery to preserve the correct logical sequence of the exhibits. In every Case there is a dark corner in which certain kinds of ware could not reasonably be placed. We have, however, been able to keep the principal groups within their respective Bays and the inconsistencies of arrangement have been confined to minor details.

The K'ang Hsi polychromes are exhibited in Bay XXXI and Standard-case F. In the former will be seen the smaller specimens which make an excellent study series; and in the latter, some magnificent examples of the larger and more sumptuous pieces. They will be found to carry on the Ming traditions, with certain modifications. There are a few specimens of the *wan li wu ts'ai*, or five-colour decoration of Wan Li type, with on-glaze enamels supported by underglaze blue. There is a series illustrating enamelling on the biscuit and another enamelling on the glaze; and there are a few pieces with decorations in coloured glazes both of the high-fired and the softer lead-silicate kinds.

The most important groups are those with on-biscuit and on-glaze enamels. These are commonly described as *famille verte*, the green family, because of the preponderance of greens of various shades in the colour scheme. The main differences between the Ming and K'ang Hsi enamelled wares are the prevalence in the latter of a cobalt-blue enamel of violet tint, which superseded the Ming turquoise green, and a more extensive use of the composite green-black. Moreover, the yellow enamel is generally purer and clearer, the iron-red is thinner and of a more coral tint, and gilding is more frequently added.

FIG. 109. Dish: K'ang Hsi *famille verte*. D. 10 in.

The *famille verte porcelain enamelled on the glaze* includes a number of pieces of the better class of export ware (figs. 106–8). This is recognized by the shapes—plates and dishes with flat rims for condiments, jugs with lip-spouts, tea and coffee cups and saucers, vases belonging to mantelpiece sets, &c. They have the characteristics of their kind as described above (p. 74), and the enamels are generally of the brilliant, jewel-like quality which lends distinction even to indifferent designs. A dish with lotus design (fig. 109) is in more orthodox Chinese taste.

Panel decoration plays a prominent part in the *famille verte* porcelain, the panels being set in a ground of richly enamelled

PLATE XIV

Fɪɢ. 110. Dish: late K'ang Hsi period. D. 22·8 in.

brocade pattern or of brilliant powder-blue (see p. 86). Favourite brocade patterns are those with flowers, symbols, butterflies, &c., scattered on a green ground which is powdered with dots, small circles, or curled scrolls in brown: others have a coral-red ground with reserved floral scrolls in white (fig. 111) or coloured. These brocades are often cut up as it were into narrow strips and used as borders.

The enamels are sometimes seen with indifferent effect on other glazes beside the white. A *lang yao* green[1] bowl and a Nanking yellow[2] bowl are decorated in this fashion; and so are a *rouleau* or club-shaped vase and an octagonal vase[3] in Standard-case F, the latter of which has panel decorations as well. Other important specimens in the last-named Case are an octagonal vase with finely drawn figures of the Eight Immortals,[4] a *kuan yin* vase[5] with large red fishes and a splendid dish (22·5 inches in diameter) with the familiar design of a pheasant on a rock (fig. 110). This last was evidently made late in the K'ang Hsi period to judge from the brown and gold border and the appearance of a rose pink (derived from gold), the first sign of the coming *famille rose*.

FIG. 111. Tankard in coral red with white scrolls. H. 6·3 in.

It will be noticed that on several of the specimens, in this and in other parts of the Collection, the mark of the Dresden Collection is found to be engraved. The Dresden Collection was formed mainly by Augustus the Strong between the years 1694 and 1705 and is now exhibited in the Johanneum at Dresden. It is unlikely that any additions were made to it after the Yung Chêng period, so that it has an unusual interest for the student; and the specimens which have come out at sales of duplicates or by other means are much prized as standards of comparison.

The combination of *famille verte* enamels with underglaze blue is a survival from the Ming period. One choice specimen, a bowl, is marked with the reign-name of Ch'êng Hua, as though to emphasize this fact; and the typical style of the *wan li wu ts'ai* (see p. 51) is seen on a few other bowls. A similar technique is

---

[1] See p. 84.   [2] See p. 87.
[3] Postcard series, C 8, No. 117.   [4] Ibid., No. 114.
[5] Ibid., No. 116. The Chinese term for a typical K'ang Hsi shape with slender oval body, contracted neck, and spreading mouth.

observable in another small group.[v] It is composed of the Chinese Imari, which, as its name implies, is Chinese porcelain decorated in the style of the Japanese 'Imari' ware (see p. 161). A free use of underglaze blue, coral red, and gilding characterizes the bulk of this ware (fig. 112); but there are also pieces decorated with enamel colours only, in what is known as the Kakiemon

FIG. 112. Covered bowl: 'Chinese Imari'.
H. 4·8 in.

style. It is easy to mistake this class of porcelain at a casual glance for Japanese, but examination of the paste and glaze and the quality of the blue will reveal its real nature to the trained eye.

In the later years of the long reign of K'ang Hsi Chinese taste seems to have favoured a refined and delicate porcelain painted in thin *famille verte* enamels from which blue is noticeably absent. This type is well illustrated by examples from the Harvey Hadden and Reginald Cory Collections (figs. 113 and 114), which include a small 'birthday plate' with the Imperial birthday greeting *wan shou wu chiang* (a myriad longevities without ending) in the border. It is usually marked with the six-character mark of the reign.

Examples of *famille verte porcelain enamelled on the biscuit* are seen in Bay XXXI. The porcelain in this case is fired without glaze. The decoration is then outlined on it in black or brown pigment and filled in with washes of transparent enamels which are fired in the usual fashion in the muffle-kiln. As compared with the on-glaze enamels the colours on this kind of ware have a softer and more subdued effect, the mat surface of the biscuit reflecting less light than the shining white glaze. Further the contrast between the bright colours and the white porcelain is generally lost, because it was deemed advisable to cover up the biscuit completely.

An exception to this will be seen in the sculptured objects, figures, &c., in which the flesh parts are uncovered. But even in this case traces of red pigment will often be found, the medium for oil-gilding with which the bare parts had been subsequently

FIG. 113. Imperial 'birthday' plate. Late K'ang Hsi period. D. 5·7 in.

FIG. 114. *Famille verte* bowl. Late K'ang Hsi period. D. 7·9 in.

coloured. Incidentally the on-biscuit decoration was specially suited for statuettes and elaborately moulded porcelains, the sharp details of which were less liable to be obscured by the thin washes of transparent enamel than by the double thickness of enamel and glaze.

As already noted this style of decoration was used by the Ming potters, and for this reason it was for a long time indiscriminately labelled Ming. If any evidence were needed to confute this obvious fallacy, it is abundantly supplied by the Dresden Col-

FIG. 115. Ink-pallet, enamelled on the biscuit: dated 1692. L. 5·2 in.

lection in which there are quantities of this ware known to have been imported at the end of the seventeenth century. Actual dated specimens are extremely rare; and so special interest in this connexion attaches to the ink-pallet (fig. 115), a typical example of the on-biscuit decoration and dated the thirty-first year of K'ang Hsi. A rare bottle-shaped vase in Standard-case F, south side, with dragons in relief on the shoulder and figures of the Eight Immortals in a wave pattern is perhaps a little earlier.

The on-biscuit enamelling on a grand scale is seen in the splendid jars and vases in Standard-case F. Here we have the composite green-black used as a ground colour in which are finely drawn designs of season flowers, blossoming fruit trees, &c., in green, aubergine, yellow, and greenish white, and some-times coral red and violet blue. Where the coral red is used it was found better to apply a patch of white glaze locally to receive it.

These black-ground porcelains (figs. 116, 117) are commonly known as *famille noire* and there is a remarkable series of them in the Collection including two noble covered jars of *potiche* form, a

PLATE XV

Fig. 116. Vase with prunus design: K'ang Hsi *famille noire*;
Ch'êng Hua mark. H. 27 in.

tall *yen yen* vase[1] beautifully decorated with a flowering prunus tree and birds, and a square vase with the flowers of the four seasons (lotus, peony, chrysanthemum, and prunus).

Another variety of this biscuit-enamelled ware has a yellow ground and is sometimes distinguished as *famille jaune*. An important specimen of this is the square, lute-shaped vase in Standard-case F, decorated in unusual style with landscape subjects (fig. 119). In another and smaller group the background is green, varying in shade from deep cucumber green to pale

Fig. 121. Pair of lions: K'ang Hsi porcelain with coloured glazes.
H. 3·8 in.

apple green: this type is represented by a vase of exceptional quality (fig. 118) in the centre of the same Standard-case.

Decoration in coloured glazes was used on K'ang Hsi porcelain though not perhaps to the same extent as on the Ming. There are a few specimens (among the biscuit-enamelled wares) with the softer lead-silicate glazes—a brush-rest in the form of a literary man seated, flanked by two figures of the Immortals Chang-kuo Lao and Ts'ao Kuo-ch'iu and two lions and a box-like ornament with a cock and peony in full relief (figs. 122–5). This last piece is part of the Sloane Collection which was given to the Museum in 1753. The difference between these coloured glazes on the biscuit and the enamels similarly applied is not very marked, but it is emphasized here by their juxtaposition. Of the harder lead-silicate glazes, turquoise and aubergine are still found in combination on figures, wine pots, &c,

High-fired glazes are used in another kind of polychrome.

[1] A Chinese name for the tall beaker with baluster body, high neck, and trumpet mouth.

Celadon green appears in combination with other glazes and colours, e.g. with blue on some small figures and with underglaze red and blue painting on vases in Standard-case G. Again two high-shouldered bottles have blue glaze on the body and painted designs in blue and underglaze red on the neck; and a

FIGS. 122, 123, 124, and 125. K'ang Hsi porcelain with coloured glazes.
FIG. 126. Horse, enamelled on the biscuit: yellow ground. L. 5·3 in.

Nanking yellow glaze will be seen in various combinations, viz. with underglaze blue, with bands of buff crackle, with *famille verte* enamels, and with gilding. The golden brown glaze, known as Nanking yellow, is one of a family of lustrous metallic brown (*tzŭ chin*) glazes described on p. 87.

From the glazes used in combination one passes in natural sequence to the glazes used singly. *K'ang Hsi monochromes* are exhibited mainly in Bay XXX and Standard-case G; but there are a few white porcelains distributed among the cases of Bay XXXI.

White is the colour for the table wares used during the period of
mourning in China and also for the altar service in the worship
of the Year-star; and at all periods fine white porcelain was
required and supplied. On the plain surface any defect or stain
would be conspicuous, and great care was required to make the
white ware flawless. As a consequence the finer white porcelains
are among the most exquisite creations of the Chinese potter.
The specimens in Bay XXXI are of uneven quality. They
include two figures of Taoist Immortals of provincial make and
a few examples of very choice pierced (*ling lung*) work which

Figs. 127, 128, and 129. Figures of an Arhat and a lion in biscuit;
white-glazed teapot (H. 4 in.).

may be earlier than K'ang Hsi, a vase with designs in white slip,
some export table ware, and an interesting series of biscuit
figures, including three Arhats and a pair of Buddhist lions (figs.
127, 129) stamped with the names of the potters Chiang Ming-
kao and Ch'ên Kuo-chih. Two of the Arhats belong to the
Sloane Collection which was given to the nation in 1753.

Other white porcelains of this kind are a handsome double-
gourd vase (fig. 130) with engraved designs in Standard-case G,
and a shallow incense-bowl[w] in Bay XXX. The latter is of
beautiful soft-looking creamy white material, with a body of
earthen appearance, known by the Chinese as *chiang t'ai* (paste
bodied), and by Western collectors as 'soft paste', and a glaze
recalling that of the finer *t'u ting* wares (see p. 33), of which it is
evidently a remote descendant.

The accumulated traditions of the Ming porcelains reinforced
by new inventions and improvements resulted in an immense
variety of coloured glazes in the K'ang Hsi and succeeding
periods; and it is frequently difficult, sometimes impossible, to
ascertain the particular reign of the Ch'ing dynasty in which a

single-coloured specimen was made. Many of the glazes continued in use with little or no change, and the only distinguishing features are to be looked for in the shape of the vessel and its general style. In view of the proverbial conservatism of the Chinese craftsmen, attributions based on such considerations must necessarily be guarded.

Many of these monochromes are *high-fired glazes* like the

ordinary white felspathic glaze, which we have already discussed, but tinted with metallic oxides. The principal colours are: (1) celadon green, a pale sea-green colour derived from iron and sometimes toned with a pinch of cobalt blue. It is similar to the old Lungchüan glaze, but the Kingtehchen celadons are readily distinguished by their white porcelain body. This is well shown by two choice vases given by Mr. Harvey Hadden. Another high-fired green glaze, in colour something between apple green and celadon, is the true *lang yao* green (see below), sometimes known as 'copper celadon'. It appears in fact to be an accidental result of misfiring a copper-red glaze of the *lang yao* type. There is a bowl of this colour in Bay XXXI, which has been painted over with *famille verte* enamels.

Fig. 130. Gourd-shaped vase, white porcelain, engraved with bats and clouds. H. 18 in.

(2) The typical K'ang Hsi red monochrome is the *lang yao*, doubtless so called from the name of a family of potters who were noted for their success with this difficult colour. It is in fact the K'ang Hsi version of the *chi hung* of the Hsüan Tê period (q.v.), a brilliant red derived from copper, the despair of the later Ming potters. The *lang yao* glaze is faintly crackled and full of minute bubbles, and the red colour appears to lie on the body in a 'dust of minute particles which the glaze has dragged downward in its flow and spread out in a continuous mass'. Where the colour and the glaze have run thick, the particles emerge in a mottling or dappling not unlike that of the powder-blue and other *soufflé* glazes. The colour is not evenly distributed, but tends to run downwards, collecting in thick masses like congealed blood on the shoulders and lower edges of vases, and conversely to shade

PLATE XVI

Figs. 118, 119, and 120. Vase with green ground; vase with yellow ground (H. 20·5 in.); and square vase with season flowers, *famille noire*. K'ang Hsi period

off and even disappear at the mouth and on the sloping sides. The flow of the glaze is well controlled in the K'ang Hsi specimens, and it does not overrun the foot-rim as on the later versions of this ware; and the glaze under the base varies from crackled green or buff to plain white. There is much variety in the *lang yao* reds as can be seen even in the few specimens in Bay XXX. The high-shouldered bottle is a fine specimen with brilliant cherry red on the sides, and thick, coagulated masses of ox-blood colour at the shoulder and above the base.[1] The same qualities are seen in the splendid baluster vase (fig. 131) given by the Keechong Hong, while on the two bowls the glaze is not so thick and the red has a crushed-strawberry tint. On the base of one of these bowls the glaze is of the typical *lang yao* green colour, perhaps due to copper which has not developed into red.

FIG. 131. *Lang yao* vase. K'ang Hsi period. H. 16·25 in.

The copper ingredient is capable of producing many other colours beside red and green under varying conditions of firing; and a glaze intended to be red sometimes emerged from the kiln with streaks and splashes of purple, grey, and blue. These variegated effects, at first accidental, are called *yao pien* (furnace transmutations) by the Chinese, who eventually learnt how to produce them at will. Hence the whole family of splashed and mottled glazes to which the French give the expressive name of *flambé*. These adventitious colours do not appear on the *lang yao*, but they are not infrequent on the later reds of the same class. Probably the K'ang Hsi potters suppressed any piece which was 'marred by this defect'. It may be added that copper-red was used for painted decoration under the glaze, often in combination with underglaze blue. The bowl,[x] with dragon designs and the K'ang Hsi mark in Bay XXXI, is a good example of the painted red. The Yung Chêng and Ch'ien Lung potters were specially successful with this kind of decoration; and specimens of various periods will be seen in Bay XXXI, Standard-case G, south side, among the snuff-bottles in Bay XXVIII and elsewhere.

[1] Postcard series, C 8, No. 119.

Another precious glaze derived from copper is the 'peach-bloom', a pinkish red which is nearly always broken by mottlings and spots of green and russet brown. A brush-washer from the Harvey Hadden Collection (fig. 132) and a beehive-shaped water-pot given by the Keechong Hong are examples of this glaze. The 'liver colour' glaze, though also tinted with copper, was apparently easier to control. It is as a rule evenly distributed, but it varies much in tone and quality. The little wine-cups in Bay XXX are attractive examples of the finer and more crimson variety of this glaze.

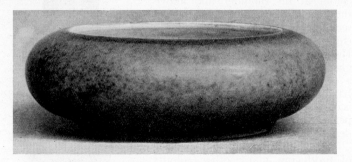

FIG. 132. 'Peach-bloom' water-pot. K'ang Hsi period. D. 4·6 in.

(3) Many shades of blue, both light and dark, were obtained by mixing cobalt with the white felspathic glaze. Other allied tints such as slaty blue, deep lavender, and pale *clair de lune* were obtained by slight modifications of this mixture. In all these cases the colouring matter permeates and suffuses the whole glaze. In another group of blues, the colour is brushed, sponged, or blown on to the body of the ware, and the glaze, subsequently added, does not absorb the colour in the same way. It remains, in fact, lying on the body, as in the blue and white porcelains, and in this condition it seems to gain in depth and brilliancy. The most celebrated of these body blues is the powder-blue which the Chinese call *ch'ui ch'ing* (blown blue) because it was blown on to the ware in a fine powder through gauze stretched over the end of a bamboo tube. When this was glazed and fired an intense and brilliant blue resulted from the aggregation of tiny specks of cobalt which still retained their powdery formation. This *ch'ui ch'ing* is included in the list of *Ts'ang yao* or special porcelains made under Ts'ang Ying-hsüan in the K'ang Hsi period. This does not absolutely prove that the process was not known before; though it would be hard to find any evidence of it on Ming porcelain, unless we see it in the bowls with 'sponged blue' mentioned in the footnote on p. 68.

The powder-blue is almost always relieved by gilt traceries: see Standard-case G, top. Its use in combination with *famille verte* enamels (fig. 133) was discussed on p. 77.

(4) The metallic-looking and lustrous brown (*tzŭ chin*) glazes form another considerable group. Their colour, like the celadon green, is obtained by mixing ferruginous earth with the white porcelain glaze; and they vary widely in tint from dark coffee-brown to the pale golden brown which goes by the name of Nanking yellow. Like the powder-blue these brown glazes are often used as surrounds for painted panels and medallions;[1] and the Nanking yellow is sometimes used as the actual ground for *famille verte* decoration (see p. 77). Again in Bay XXXI there is a dish with coffee-brown glaze with designs in silver. The use of silver in decoration is claimed as one of T'ang Ying's innovations at the Imperial factory (i.e. after 1728): but Père d'Entrecolles, writing in 1722, specifically refers to silver decoration on a lustrous brown glaze. The lustrous brown glaze was also variegated by crackle (see below).

FIG. 133. Bottle with powder-blue ground and *famille verte* panels. H. 11·5 in.

The same ferruginous ingredient combined with a little cobalti-ferous ore of manganese was used to make the 'mirror black' (*wu chin*) glaze, a beautiful lustrous black with reflections sometimes of soft brown, sometimes of bluish tone. Used as a monochrome this glaze is generally relieved by gilding. Père d'Entrecolles asserts that the *wu chin* glaze is an invention of the K'ang Hsi period. This is certainly true in the sense that it differs some-what from any other lustrous black glaze, but it is in reality no very distant relation of the old brown-black glazes of *temmoku* type found on Sung and Ming wares.

It will be observed that many of the Chinese monochrome glazes are fissured with a network of cracks more or less regularly disposed. As both body and glaze expand in the heat of the kiln

[1] Porcelain of this kind is sometimes called 'Batavian ware', because much of it was imported by the Dutch who had a settlement and entrepôt of their far-eastern trade at Batavia, in Java.

and contract when cooling, a slight difference in the rate of shrinkage of body and glaze will result in a crackling of the glaze. This no doubt often occurred accidentally, but the Chinese potters learnt at an early date how to produce crackle at will and even to regulate its size, and it became a distinctive feature of some of their wares. It is clear that more than one method was employed to produce the crackle (figs. 160, 161); but the simplest seems to have been the admixture of a certain stone (perhaps steatite) in the glaze which disturbed the ratio of contraction between the body and the glaze in the manner desired. Thus Père d'Entrecolles frequently refers to *sui yu*, or crackle glaze, as mixed with the browns and blues where crackle was required. Some of the later crackled glazes professedly copy the old Sung types; the buff and grey crackles being classed as Ko glazes, and others as Kuan. It should be noted that this intentional crackle is quite distinct from the accidental crazing which takes place in many glazes after long use and is almost always present in the lead-silicate glazes.

The lead-silicate glazes, which were fired at a lower temperature than the felspathic (see p. 49), are represented among the K'ang Hsi monochromes by a beautiful turquoise, a dark violet aubergine, and a yolk-of-egg yellow.

Examples of K'ang Hsi enamels used as monochromes are not common. The transparent green was used over a grey crackle to form the so-called 'apple-green';[1] and there are several composite greens—camellia-leaf, sage, &c.—apparently formed in a similar way, but these appear to be mostly of Ch'ien Lung make. The composite green-black of the *famille verte* is occasionally found in monochrome; and the iron-red was frequently used in this way, but most of the known specimens of it are of post-K'ang Hsi date.

Blue and White. Blue and white porcelain enjoyed an immense popularity in the K'ang Hsi period in both the home and foreign markets. It evidently formed the principal item of an extensive export trade, for Père d'Entrecolles, writing in 1712, asserts that one hardly sees any other kind of Chinese porcelain in Europe. It certainly bulks largely in all European collections and that of the British Museum is no exception. The secret of its success was excellence of manufacture which is apparent even in the export wares. The body of the ware is a clean white material of the finest grain: a special glaze was used, and the combined effect is a beautiful solid white like well-set curds. The blue with which this ware is painted varies from a deep sapphire to a pale silvery blue, but it is always pure and without the strain of grey or purple noticeable in other blues. Moreover the blue and the white blend harmoniously. We hear nothing of the importation of blue at this time, but we are told that the native cobalt

[1] This glaze is often erroneously classed with the *lang yao* (see p. 84).

mineral was refined and purified by elaborate processes and that
the different grades of blue were obtained by mixing the refined
and the unrefined cobalt in varying proportions. The main
processes of manufacture were substantially the same as those
used on the Ming blue and white; but there are obvious differences in the style of decoration and in general effect. Heavy
outlines filled in by flat washes of colour are the common Ming
characteristics: the K'ang Hsi designs are faintly outlined[1] and
filled in with graded washes which give the blue itself more life
and movement. As far as the designs themselves are concerned,
the comparison will generally be favourable to the Ming. Most
of the K'ang Hsi patterns, in fact, are borrowed from the Ming
wares, and their rendering is necessarily more mechanical because
the decorator's work was more thoroughly systematized. Each
piece passed through many hands. One painter outlined the
designs and another put in the filling washes: one drew the birds,
another the landscapes, and another the borders, and so on.
The lack of individuality which resulted from this minute division
of labour is partly compensated by the high quality of the
materials and the careful workmanship; but the outstanding
feature of the K'ang Hsi blue and white is undoubtedly the
beautiful marbled blue. After the K'ang Hsi period the manufacture of the blue and white deteriorated with the rising vogue
of the enamelled porcelains.

The series of blue and white exhibited in Bay XXX and in
Standard-case E gives a good idea of the variety in form, decoration, and quality of blue which may be looked for in this class
of ware. The saucer-dishes (fig. 135) with moulded sides, painted
in pale blue with the 'love chase' (the current name for a design
of a man and woman on horseback hunting a hare), are clearly
descendants of the crisply moulded late Ming ware with designs
in silvery blue which was mentioned on p. 61. Curiously enough
the Ming pieces of this kind are very rarely marked, while the
K'ang Hsi specimens generally have marks of the early Ming
reign of Ch'êng Hua.

It will be noticed that European forms—plates with flat rims
suitable for condiments, salt-cellars, cruets, tea and coffee cups
with saucers, and mantelpiece sets of vases—are now much in
evidence. Actual European models are occasionally used as in
the case of the bottles (fig. 134) with wing-handles obviously
copied from Venetian glass; and, as already stated, the foreign
merchants made their influence felt in the sphere of design. The
curious mark, resembling a capital G, which appears on a pair
of bottles (fig. 136) and also on *famille verte* of good quality, is
probably the trade sign of some foreign importer.

[1] This fact is clearly shown by an octagonal bowl on which the decoration
has only been partially completed.

The finer grades of blue, both light and dark, can be studied in the picked specimens in Bay XXX. Part of a set of five[1] shows what high quality of colour may be looked for even on the export wares of this time. It is painted with the familiar design of a rock and pheasant and flowering plants, and, like the tiger-lily jar below it (fig. 138), is a good example of the blue designs on a white ground. Two sprinklers and ewers (figs.

FIGS. 134, 135, 136. K'ang Hsi blue and white: bottle with wing handles, 'love chase' dish (D. 7·8 in.), and bottle with G mark.

137 and 139) in the same section, on the other hand, effectively illustrate in their panels of arabesques another method of decoration, with white designs reserved in a blue ground. This method, which gave full scope to the beautiful marbled blue, was used in the decoration of some of the most sumptuous blue and white porcelains. It is seen, for instance, on the well-known 'hawthorn' (more correctly, 'prunus') jars, of which a moderately good example (fig. 140) is exhibited in Standard-case E. Such jars were destined to carry New Year gifts of fragrant tea and sweetmeats and they were appropriately decorated with a beautiful design of flowering prunus sprays on a reticulated and marbled ground suggesting cracked ice. The New Year in China, it should be explained, comes three to seven weeks later than in our calendar, when the blossoming prunus and the breaking ice are already proclaiming the approach of Spring.

[1] The complete mantelpiece set of five consists of three covered jars and two beakers. In the present case the three beakers and two jars, though matching approximately in pattern, are parts of two sets.

FIG. 140. K'ang Hsi blue and white 'prunus jar'. H. 10·5 in.

FIGS. 137, 138, and 139. K'ang Hsi blue and white sprinkler; jar with
tiger-lily scrolls; and ewer. H. 7·2 in.

Next to the prunus jar are two cylindrical vases of good quality
(fig. 141) decorated also in white on blue; and above it is a fine
set of five—three covered jars and two beakers (fig. 143). In
other parts of the Standard-case, which is mainly filled with
objects of large size, are some good examples of vases, covered
jars, and dishes, among which a large dish with sides moulded

FIG. 141. K'ang Hsi blue
and white jar. H. 11 in.

FIG. 142. K'ang Hsi blue and
white beaker with magnolia
design. H. 18 in.

in oblique foliations and covered with tiger-lily scrolls is worthy
of note; and the magnolia beaker (fig. 142) illustrates an effective
treatment of the design in which the white blooms stand out
against a backing of colour.

A few specimens of late Ming and transition blue and white
have been placed for convenience in the Table-case and under it,
but the bulk of the exhibits here are the smaller K'ang Hsi
specimens. Among them is an interesting series of objects
recovered from wrecks in Table Bay by Henry Adams and his
divers in 1853. They are part of the cargoes of old East India-
men; and though we know that one was the *Haarlem* (lost in
1648), it is unfortunately impossible to say now to which ship
any particular piece belonged. The series as a whole, however,

PLATE XVII

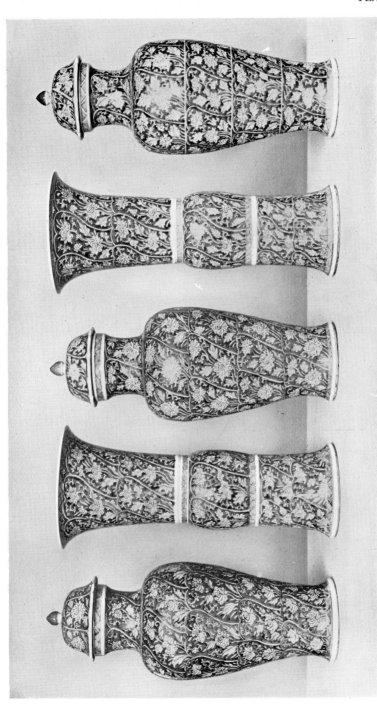

Fig. 143. Set of five K'ang Hsi blue and white vases. H. 20·4 in.

may be taken as typical of the commoner type of export goods in the middle and latter parts of the seventeenth century (figs. 144, 145, 146). It includes tea ware of thin, moulded porcelain, like that of the 'love chase' dishes (p. 89), with familiar designs such as single figures of graceful ladies commonly known as 'long Elizas', vases, growing flowers, children, &c. The marks on the Table Bay pieces include the reign-marks of K'ang Hsi and Ch'êng Hua and a few marks of the complimentary kind.

It may be observed here that a great variety of marks are

FIGS. 144, 145, and 146. Blue and white porcelain recovered from wrecks in Table Bay. H. of jar 6·5 in.

found on the K'ang Hsi blue and white, among which the reign-mark of the period is one of the least common. This is partly explained by an edict of the district magistrate in 1677 (recorded in the *T'ao lu*) forbidding the potters to inscribe the reign-name of the Emperor or any sacred writing on their porcelain, lest it should be broken or defaced; and although it is not clear how long this ordinance remained in force, it is noticeable that the bulk of the earlier K'ang Hsi porcelain is marked either with the reign-names of Ming emperors or with hall-marks, symbols, and marks of commendation (see p. 170), such as *yü* (jade), *ya* (elegant), &c.

It remains to mention a special type of blue and white which was made in great perfection not only in the K'ang Hsi but in the Yung Chêng and Ch'ien Lung periods. The most interesting explanation of it is given by Père d'Entrecolles writing from Kingtehchen in 1722: 'The porcelain made with *hua shih* is rare and far more expensive than the other porcelain. It has an extremely fine grain: and for purposes of painting, when compared with ordinary porcelain, it is almost as vellum to paper.

Some of the potters do not use *hua shih* for the body of the ware, but content themselves with making a diluted slip into which they dip their porcelain when dry, so as to give it a coating of the material before it is painted and glazed.' The composition of the body is given as eight parts of *hua shih* to two of china stone (*petuntse*). This *hua shih* was identified by Père d'Entrecolles as soapstone or steatite,[1] and for this reason the term 'steatitic' has been adopted on the labels in preference to the current, but

Fig. 147. Bowl with figures of Immortals. 'Steatitic' porcelain. D. 5·8 in.

misleading, 'soft-paste'. A choice example of the ware is an incense bowl (with carved wooden cover) which shows its characteristics, viz. an opaque body, in colour like earthenware but of very fine texture, and a soft-looking crackled glaze (fig. 147). Other and later specimens will be noted elsewhere.

YUNG CHÊNG

(1723–35)

DURING the brief but ceramically important reign of Yung Chêng (1723–35) the control of the Imperial factory was in the competent hands of Nien Hsi-yao, Inspector of Customs at Huai-an Fu (Hwaian); and in the latter part of the period Nien had the assistance of the celebrated T'ang Ying who was appointed to the works in 1728 and served a voluntary apprenticeship of three years before taking up the management..

The Yung Chêng potters inherited a rich legacy in the tradi-

[1] Vogt, however, who analysed samples of *hua shih* from San-pao-p'êng, declared it to be a kind of pegmatite.

tions of the preceding reigns; and, though much attention was given to imitating masterpieces of the past, many new ideas and many modifications of existing processes will be noticed in their wares. The reign was a time of transition from the broad K'ang Hsi style to the meticulous and rather precious art of the Ch'ien Lung period; but the Yung Chêng wares have a peculiar elegance both in form and decoration and are not lacking in distinction.

If we may judge from the few marked specimens in Bay XXX,

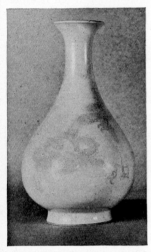

Fig. 148. Bottle with 'scratched blue' design. H. 7·5 in.

Fig. 149. Cup and saucer painted by Yang-lin. D. 4·5 in.

the blue and white is but a shadow of the K'ang Hsi ware. The same patterns appear, but the blue lacks quality and there are indications that the ware no longer received the same attention as before. On the other hand, much care was expended on imitations of the Ming types, the Ming peculiarities being copied closely enough to cause no little perplexity to modern collectors.

The interesting list of decorations used at the Imperial factory which was compiled by T'ang Ying while Hsieh Min was Governor of Kiangsi (1729–34), shows that ancient specimens from the Palace and other sources were sent to Kingtehchen to be copied. There is not space here to enumerate the fifty-eight items of this important list, which will be found in the more exhaustive works on Chinese porcelain: but allusion will be made to it from time to time under the title of the Yung Chêng List.

A peculiar kind of blue and white in which the blue colour was apparently rubbed into an incised design is seen on two vases (fig. 148); though bearing the Ch'êng Hua mark they are made of a fine white, glassy porcelain which seems to have been a special composition introduced in the Yung Chêng period or just before it. Painted ornament in underglaze red, by itself or in company with underglaze blue, was freely and successfully used; good examples are shown on the south side of Standard-case G.

In the enamelled wares, the *famille verte* style of decoration, though not entirely discontinued, gave way to the new *famille rose* colour scheme; but in the process of transition it left behind a small group of a very distinctive kind of which the covered bowl (fig. 150) is an example. The designs are carefully painted

FIGS. 150 and 151. Yung Chêng covered bowl enamelled over blue; and bowl with underglaze blue and red, and white slip. D. 7·8 in.

in underglaze blue and then covered with delicate washes of pale *famille verte* enamels. This kind of decoration, however, is not a K'ang Hsi type, but a revival of a Ming style which probably originated in the Ch'êng Hua period. The Chinese name for it is *tou ts'ai*.

Another decoration which belongs to this reign is done in iron-red and gold; and yet another is painted in dry black, resembling Indian ink, or in black and gold. This is the *ts'ai shui mo* (decoration in ink) of the Yung Chêng List, and Père d'Entrecolles tells us that painting in actual ink was at first attempted but was of course a failure.

The *famille rose*, now become fashionable, takes its name from an opaque ruby-pink enamel derived from gold (purple of cassius) which made its first appearance as a rather muddy rose colour towards the end of the K'ang Hsi period. It is seen, for instance, in small quantities in the handsome dish (fig. 110); and if we may judge from a bowl in the Table-case of Bay XXIX which bears a cyclical mark (= A.D. 1721) and its companion saucer (fig. 154), it was already well developed by the end of that reign. This again is borne out by the palace bowls from the Reginald Cory bequest which have the Imperial form of the K'ang Hsi

mark (*k'ang hsi yü chih*). In the Yung Chêng period this rose
colour was developed in a variety of shades; and a palette of
opaque enamels, many of them mixed colours, was formed which
was generally adopted in place of the *famille verte*. The *famille
rose* enamels were evidently regarded by the Chinese as something exotic and they are variously named *juan ts'ai* (soft colours)
and *yang ts'ai* (foreign colours).[1] The few specimens of *famille*

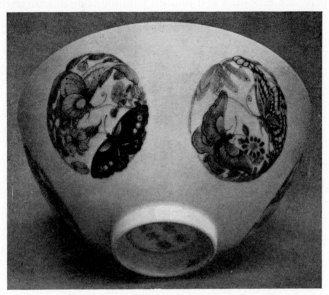

FIG. 152. Bowl. Yung Chêng period. D. 5·2 in.

rose painting in Bay **XXX** illustrate the ordinary types. One, a
dish from the Dresden Collection with an elegant spray of
flowers, though rather coarsely painted, illustrates an attractive
Yung Chêng style of decoration in which a slight but graceful
floral design is artistically thrown on to the white ground. Others
from the Reginald Cory bequest include a bowl and a dish with
peach boughs and a small bowl beautifully decorated with
butterfly medallions (fig. 152).

But the full development of the *famille rose* palette is seen in the
Table-case of Bay **XXIX** in the fine series of eggshell dishes and
table wares given to the Museum by Sir A. W. Franks and the
Hon. Robert Meade. Most of these richly ornamented wares
were destined for the European market, and decorated (but not

[1] Reference to European, or foreign, decoration occurs in no less than six
items in the Yung Chêng List.

actually made) at Canton by the artists who painted the Canton enamels on copper. The usual decoration consists of a panel, painted with miniature-like delicacy with groups of ladies and children in an interior, or with rockery and pheasants, cocks and peonies, flowering plants, &c., enclosed by borders of rich diaper patterns, sometimes as many as seven in number.[1] The backs of plates and saucers are often coated with ruby pink. These wares display skilful potting and finished painting; but their over-rich

FIG. 153. Yung Chêng 'eggshell' plate. D. 8·3 in.

colour and rather effeminate style present a striking contrast with the bold and vigorous *famille verte* decoration.

The Table-case contains many first-rate specimens including some with 'ruby backs' and 'seven borders', and a few documentary pieces which help to fix the date of the ware. One of the last, a bowl with rose-enamelled exterior and a spray of flowers and fruit within, bears a cyclical date corresponding to the year 1721 (see p. 170): an octagonal plate has the mark of the Dresden Collection which implies a date not later than the Yung Chêng period; and a saucer 'with lady and children, vases and furniture', and a straight-sided cup with black and gold decoration have the Yung Chêng mark. There are, besides, a few specimens among the armorial porcelains (in Bay VI) with supplementary decoration in Canton style which can be dated to the period by their armorial bearings, and one cup and saucer

[1] Postcard series, C 8, No. 120.

inscribed with the actual date 1728. Other interesting pieces are the saucer (fig. 155) finely decorated with a 'Canton painting' signed Pai-shih; and another (fig. 149) with the mark, on the base, of the decorator Yang-lin of Yu-fang (an old name for Kunshan).

But the choicest enamelled porcelain of the Yung Chêng and early Ch'ien Lung periods is neither pure *famille verte* nor *famille rose*. It is a blend of the two, a beautiful dead-white glassy ware delicately painted in mixed enamels, some translucent and some

YUNG CHÊNG *famille rose.*—FIG. 154. Stand for bowl. D. 6 in.
FIG. 155. Dish with a 'Canton painting' by Pai-shih. D. 6·2 in.

opaque. This is the porcelain to which Chinese collectors have attached the name Ku-yüeh-hsüan, unfortunately without being able to agree as to its meaning and origin. It is evidently an Imperial ware, painted sometimes with designs showing European influence (see p. 75) and sometimes in pure Chinese taste, the decoration being completed by a stanza of verse with red seals attached; and the reign-mark is generally added in a thick blue enamel. Good examples of this porcelain[1] are rare outside China, and at present it is unrepresented in the Collection.

The porcelain with coloured glazes made at this time is of special interest because we learn from the Yung Chêng List that the old Sung glazes—the Ju, Kuan, Ko, Lungchüan, Chün, and Ting—were carefully copied, and it is certain that this revival of the Sung monochromes was not confined to the Imperial factory. There are several Yung Chêng monochromes in Bay

[1] A remarkable series was lent by the Chinese Government to the Exhibition at Burlington House 1935–6; see Catalogue 2103, 2105, 2118, 2152, &c.

XXX, including imitations of the old Kuan glaze, and buff and grey crackles of Ko type, besides sage green, lustrous brown, yellow, liver red, and red *flambé*. A variety of the red *flambé* designed to imitate the variegated Chün ware (see p. 27) is seen on two bulb-bowls. Not only the glaze but the shapes of these pieces and, in one case, the incised numeral mark are in close imitation of the Sung Chün. Among the monochromes in

Figs. 156–8. Figures of a hawk, crane (H. 18·5 in.), and cock, early 18th century.

Standard-case G are a handsome bottle with a speckled red glaze of liver tint with the mark of the Yung Chêng period, a few grey crackles which imitate Sung glazes, and a fine yellow dish with engraved designs.

CH'IEN LUNG

(1736–95)

THE long and prosperous reign of Ch'ien Lung (1736–95) was the last of the great periods of Chinese ceramic history. The celebrated T'ang Ying was now appointed to the supreme control of the Imperial factory; and during his rule, which ended in

1749, the Kingtehchen potters touched the zenith of their skill. The Imperial porcelains were marvels of technique. The potters were masters of their trade. They were now able to control the difficult *flambé* glaze effects (fig. 159) which had hitherto been a matter of chance, and they found scope for their ingenuity in the imitations of all manner of alien substances such as patinated bronze, jade and other stones, shells, grained wood, lacquer, and

FIG. 159. Dish in the form of a bat with *flambé* red glaze. L. 10·3 in.

cloisonné enamel. It was, moreover, a great period for collections of antiques, the Emperor himself being an enthusiastic antiquarian; and this resulted in the archaizing tendency noticeable in the minor arts of the time, the ceramic being no exception. Thus the forms of vessels and their surface ornament are often copied from antique bronzes; and doubtless the imitations of the old Sung and Ming wares, a specialty of the preceding reign, continued unabated. On the other hand, a great deal of the Ch'ien Lung enamelled ware in modern collections betrays obvious European influences. Trade with the West was in full swing, and a vast quantity of porcelain was made at Kingtehchen and decorated (chiefly at Canton) for the European market.

A series of typical Ch'ien Lung porcelains can be seen in Bay XXIX. The blue and white will be compared unfavourably with the K'ang Hsi blue and white, but it is evident that this kind of ware was now out of fashion. On the other hand, there are certain types of blue painting which seem to have been prevalent. The mottled blue of the Hsüan Tê porcelain is reproduced on a ewer on the top shelf (and again on a vase with bronze form and design in Standard-case E, south side): the close floral scrolls on the marked tazza (fig. 163) recur on several specimens; and the 'steatitic porcelain' with carefully pencilled designs in good blue is represented by a variety of

FIGS. 160, 161, and 162. Two vases with crackled grey glaze; and a Ch'ien Lung vase imitating carved jade (H. 5 in.)

specimens. Some of these have an opaque 'steatitic' body and others have only a wash of the 'steatite'. A large vase, with lion and pine tree well painted in dark blue, belongs to this second class (fig. 164). Painting in underglaze red, alone and in combination with blue, was freely used; and specimens of both types may be seen in the Collection.

The enamelled wares are more numerous and varied; but they nearly all conform to the *famille rose* type. Reds and pinks are prominent and many of the pieces are elaborately modelled and decorated with openwork and encrusted flowers. The two Buddha figures on pedestals, decorated with rather tight floral scrolls in the manner of the cloisonné-enamel temple wares, are characteristically Ch'ien Lung: while the beaker (fig. 166) has a wash of an opaque bluish green enamel in the mouth and under the base, a colour which occurs frequently from the Ch'ien Lung period onwards. Above them are specimens of 'graviata'

FIG. 163. Blue and white stem-cup:
Ch'ien Lung mark. H. 4·3 in.

FIG. 164. Ch'ien Lung blue
and white vase with 'steatitic'
wash. H. 17 in.

FIGS. 165, 166, and 167. Ch'ien Lung enamelled porcelain.
H. of flask 5 in.

Fig. 168. 'Lace-work' bottle, H. 7 in.

Fig. 169. 'Rice-grain' vase, H. 7·7 in.

wares which were a novelty of their time, vases and bowls with grounds of opaque pink, green, blue, and yellow engraved all over with feathery scrollwork. There are a few *famille rose* specimens of this period in the lower part of Standard-case F, south side, and among them two plates with silvered designs, a novelty ascribed, but on doubtful grounds (see p. 87), to T'ang Ying. In the same Case will be seen a bottle-shaped vase coated with

FIG. 170. Bottle with black lacquer inlaid with mother-of-pearl. H. 14·5 in.

FIG. 171. Vase. Ch'ien Lung period. H. 20·6 in.

black lacquer in which are inlaid designs in mother-of-pearl (fig. 170). This is the *porcelaine laquée burgautée* of French collectors, of which there are other specimens in Bay XXX, one perhaps of K'ang Hsi date.

Two other novel types of decoration will be observed in Bay XXIX: (1) 'lace-work', a name given to the ornament on a marked tazza and a vase which is deeply incised, then covered and filled in by a greenish-white glaze (fig. 168); and (2) 'rice-grain', a kindred type but with the idea carried a stage farther, in which the pattern is expressed by a series of transparencies formed by cutting out small pieces of the paste (about the size and shape of a grain of rice) and allowing the glaze to fill up the perforations. Specimens of this work (fig. 169) bear the marks of the Ch'ien Lung and succeeding reigns.

There are, besides, examples of the so-called 'Mandarin' porcelain, decorated with scrollwork in red, pink, gold, and underglaze blue surrounding panels of figures which are usually in Mandarin dress. This ware was popular with the European merchants in the last half of the eighteenth century. Some of it is of fine 'eggshell' porcelain; some has the undulating 'orange-peel'[1] glaze, which is often seen on Ch'ien Lung porcelains; other pieces are encrusted with flowers in high relief (fig. 174), while others again have the ground between the panels granulated

FIGS. 172, 173, and 174. Two vases of 'Mandarin porcelain', and Dr. Johnson's teapot (H. 8·4 in.).

like shagreen. Another well-known export type is illustrated by Dr. Johnson's capacious teapot, which is painted with panels of pink and red flowers in European taste (fig. 173). Still more obviously European decorations of this period are to be seen among the exhibits of armorial porcelain, &c., in Bay VI.

The Ch'ien Lung monochromes, which are legion, are represented by a number of type specimens in Bay XXIX and Standard-case G. The marked pieces include a pair of dishes with the dark purplish blue glaze (the colour of the tiles and of the vessels belonging to the Temple of Heaven, at Peking), a double vase of pale *clair de lune*, a tazza with liver-red passing into white, a water-pot with lustrous brown glaze and reliefs, a bowl with lustrous aubergine glaze, a square box with opaque yellowish green, and a covered bowl with opaque ruby-pink glaze; besides specimens of 'robin's egg' glaze, an opaque bluish green freckled with pink. There are, besides, unmarked

[1] An exaggerated and intentional unevenness of surface, doubtless suggested by the accidental inequalities in some of the early Ming glazes.

specimens of 'apple green', turquoise, crackled brown and buff, camellia-leaf green, a *ju-i* sceptre with sulphur-yellow glaze, and a fungus-shaped vase (fig. 162) imitating emerald-green jade. In Standard-case G are examples of the red *flambé* glazes, bronze green, tea dust, iron-rust, mirror black, &c. The list is a long one, but the Collection by no means exhausts the known

FIG. 175. 'Mille-fleurs' water-pot. Ch'ien Lung period. D. 5 in.

types of monochromes of this fertile period, which may be said to include practically every shade of colour made by the Chinese, imitations of the Sung and Ming, continuations of the K'ang Hsi and Yung Chêng specialties, and numerous novelties introduced by T'ang Ying.

CHIA CH'ING

(1796–1820)

THE Chia Ch'ing period (1796–1820) is from the ceramic point of view a prolongation of the Ch'ien Lung. The porcelains of the early part of the reign were little, if at all, inferior to the late Ch'ien Lung wares, but in the absence of any inventive enterprise the potter's art stagnated and gradually sank into a decadence which becomes more and more apparent in the course of the

nineteenth century. There are a few specimens of Chia Ch'ing
porcelain in Bay XXIX, some of which call for special comment.
A bowl with rice-grain ornament is interesting as illustrating
the blue and white of the period and as bearing the signature of
a potter, Wang Shêng-kao, and a date corresponding to 1798.
Above it is a coffee-pot with a brick-red ground (this is 'iron-red'
heavily fluxed and with a faintly dappled texture) and medallions
in *famille rose* colouring. It has a cyclical date mark which

FIGS. 176, 177, and 178. Chia Ch'ing medallion bowl, Ch'ien Lung vase
(H. 7·9 in.) and Tao Kuang bowl.

corresponds to the year 1808; and the same mark appears on
a bowl with similar red inside and similar medallions, but in a
mottled brown-black ground, outside. A bowl with reeded sides,
an Imperial piece with the Chia Ch'ing mark, is covered with
an opaque sealing-wax red enamel; and near by are 'medallion
bowls' with yellow and ruby pink grounds (fig. 176). These are
Imperial rice-bowls decorated on the exterior with opaque *famille
rose* enamels (sometimes engraved with floral scrolls or diapered
with painted scrollwork) in which are set four medallions with
designs of flowers, landscapes, &c., and sometimes with figures
in European dress. A few of these are known with Ch'ien Lung
marks, but as a rule they belong to the Chia Ch'ing and Tao
Kuang periods. A tazza or stem-cup, enamelled with Buddhist
emblems and lotus arabesques, has a Chia Ch'ing mark and an
inscription stating that it was 'respectfully presented to the Sub-
prefect of Ching-tê Chên, in Kiangsi'. As a presentation piece
it may fairly be regarded as a typical example of the enamelled
porcelain of the period. A circular box in Bay XXVIII has a

well-executed design of dragons in red and gold over a pattern
of scrolls in pale underglaze blue, and an inscribed cartouche on
the cover.

TAO KUANG

(1821–50)

A MARKED deterioration is evident in the general run of the Tao
Kuang porcelains (1821–50), both in material and decoration.
The body tends to become coarse and greyish, and the glaze has

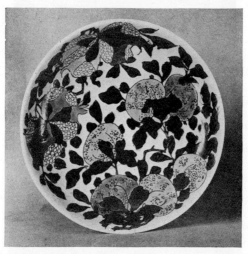

FIG. 179. Dish with design in coloured glazes over engraved dragons.
D. 9·9 in.

an exaggerated oily sheen and the 'musliny' texture which is
observable on Japanese export porcelains. There are, however,
many exceptions and much of the neatness of the Ch'ien Lung
wares is observable in the Tao Kuang Imperial pieces. This is
seen in a good series of 'medallion bowls' (often called Peking
bowls), which have fine enamelled designs outside and underglaze blue within (fig. 178). Other polychrome pieces show the
prevalence of mixed enamels at this time, i.e. combinations of
famille verte and *famille rose* colours, and also a revival of the
Ch'êng Hua style in which thin transparent enamels are laid
over underglaze blue designs. The painting is sometimes executed
with considerable delicacy, as on a rounded rice-bowl, with
design of Taoistic figures crossing the sea. On this and other
specimens of the period one notices a lustrous wash of thin
greenish white in parts of the decoration. A similar lustrous film
is seen on a saucer-dish (fig. 179) and bowl which are painted

on the biscuit with large fruits in colour over an etched dragon design. They have the K'ang Hsi mark and are possibly replace-

FIG. 180. Enamelled bowl made at the Shên-tê Hall.
D. 6·8 in.

FIG. 181. Dish with red and green enamels, 'Copy of the antique made at the Shên-tê Hall'. D. 10·5 in.

ments of an original K'ang Hsi service. A saucer-dish on the same shelf, prettily painted with a pink hawthorn bough, shows some originality in treatment.

A considerable number of the specimens in Bays XXIX and

XXVIII, which are assigned to the Tao Kuang period, have Hall-marks (see p. 170) of various kinds. One of these, the mark of the *shên tê t'ang* (Shên-tê Hall—see p. 173), which appears to have been in use during the Tao Kuang[1] period, recurs on specimens of several kinds in Bay XXIX: viz. a vase with dragon designs in a ground of opaque lavender-blue enamel, a delicately enamelled bowl (fig. 180), a 'rice-grain' dish, and two pieces which frankly imitate Ming types. One, a large saucer-dish (fig. 181), is painted with enamels of the 'red and green family' (see p. 51), and bears the illuminating mark *shên tê t'ang po ku chih* (antique made at the Shên-tê Hall); and the other, in paste, glaze, blue and design, copies closely a late Ming blue and white bowl.

The ordinary Tao Kuang blue and white is of indifferent quality, as may be seen in a few marked pieces. One of these has the signature of a potter, Wên Lang-shan, and a cyclical date corresponding to the year 1847. The marked Tao Kuang monochromes include bowls with full yellow glaze outside, a bowl with lustrous coffee-brown glaze and a vase with deep turquoise glaze. The last, which is in Standard-case G, bears a date corresponding to 1844. A large bowl in Bay XXIX is covered outside with a motley of green, yellow, aubergine, and white, in the style of the earlier 'egg and spinach' glazes.

HSIEN FÊNG (1851–61)

AND LATER

In Bay XXVIII there are among the modern porcelains a few specimens belonging to the reign of Hsien Fêng (1851–61), the best of which is the little 'wedding bowl' with medallions of appropriate symbols in a yellow ground. They were probably made at the beginning of the reign, for in 1853 the T'ai-p'ing rebels captured Kingtehchen and burnt down the Imperial factory, and sacked the town, killing and scattering the potters. The factory was rebuilt in 1864 in the reign of T'ung Chih (1862–74), and we find again a published list of the wares sent to the Palace, similar to that compiled by T'ang Ying in the Yung Chêng period. Neither the list nor surviving examples of the wares of this period display any originality. Indeed the latter show us Chinese porcelain at its lowest ebb.

In the reign of Kuang Hsü (1875–1908) there was a gradual revival, and the potters recovered enough of their former skill to make colourable imitations of the older wares. A saucer with birds and flowers in a clouded pink ground and a covered bowl,

---

[1] It occurs on a specimen in the Hippisley Collection which is inscribed with a poem by the Emperor Tao Kuang.

with spout and handle, decorated with inscriptions, are marked porcelains of this reign; and the small saucers, enamelled with lotuses and storks, have a palace-mark (*ta ya chai*) of the celebrated Empress Dowager.

Under the Republic in 1916 Yüan Shih-k'ai took over one of the former Imperial kilns and gave orders for porcelain to be made for his personal use. Specimens of this ware with delicately painted designs in enamels in the Ku-yüeh-hsüan style are known. They bear the mark *hung hsien nien chih* or *chü jên t'ang chih*.

SNUFF BOTTLES, ETC.

Two compartments in the Table-case in Bay XXVIII contain (1) a series of small objects of various kinds, and (2) a series of snuff bottles.

The former include many of those dainty little specimens in which the Chinese connoisseur delights and the Chinese potter excels. They are in the main in pure Chinese taste: the furniture of the writing table, such as vessels of fanciful form (shaped like leaves, blossoms, shells, &c.) for holding water, water-droppers for moistening the ink, brush-rests, wrist-rests, seals, boxes for holding the seal vermilion, miniature incense-burners, &c.; a tube for a Mandarin's peacock feather; a girdle hook imitating an old jade in form and substance; a hand-warmer and a wall vase with openwork sides; and a hanging perfume box,[1] in the form of a ball with pierced ornaments and designs painted in an unusual style, viz. *famille rose* enamels on the biscuit.

They are mostly of the Ch'ien Lung period or later. In making these small vessels and the snuff bottles the specialized and more costly forms of porcelain were frequently used, such as (1) the 'steatitic' or 'soft-paste' (see p. 93); (2) a ware of Ting type which we are told was made of *ch'ing tien* stone, opaque, creamy, and with an earthen-looking paste; and (3) a dead-white and glassy porcelain intended to look like semi-opaque glass.[2]

The snuff bottles are chiefly in the form of diminutive vases or flasks, though sometimes they take more fanciful shapes, viz. of animal and human figures, fruit, flowers, &c. Diminutive vases have been known from early times by the name of *yao p'ing* (medicine vases); but it is highly improbable that the orthodox porcelain snuff bottle with its spoon-stopper (usually capped with jade, precious stone, or glass) came into use before the eighteenth century. It is true that tobacco was introduced into China from Manila in 1530, but the general style of the snuff bottles is that of the eighteenth century or later. The series

---

[1] Vessels of this sort are often miscalled 'cricket pots' or 'butterfly cages'.

[2] A good example of this type of ware is the teapot[y] with arms of Maitland of Pitrichie in Bay VI.

exhibited is arranged as far as possible chronologically. Only one has a possibly genuine date as early as K'ang Hsi, many have the Yung Chêng mark, and the rest, if marked at all, have the reign-names of Ch'ien Lung, Chia Ch'ing, and Tao Kuang.

Apart from the skilful workmanship displayed, these two series are interesting for the great variety of decorative methods which they illustrate in a compendious form. One sees in the snuff bottles good examples of 'steatitic' blue and white, blue and under-glaze red painting, every form of enamelling on the glaze and

Figs. 182 and 183. Chia Ch'ing snuff bottles, creamy white porcelain. H. 3·5 in. and 3 in.

on the biscuit, numerous monochromes including mirror-black, *sang de bœuf*, tea dust, plain white and cream-whites of Ting type. One group is cleverly decorated with pierced ornament and finely carved reliefs, some of the bottles having an outer casing of elaborate openwork. Another little group illustrates various kinds of black decoration not otherwise seen in the Collection, viz. a dry black with dragon design etched out of it in white, a shiny black with white figures reserved (Tao Kuang mark) and blue and white designs in a hard enamel-black ground. They are all of a late type, the black being no longer formed by a green wash over a black pigment, but by a ready-made black enamel in which the black pigment is incorporated in the glassy flux before it is applied.

Among the nineteenth-century snuff bottles are one or two of the crude little *flacons* which have been found in Egyptian tombs, where they were doubtless dropped by natives, by accident or design. They are a reminder of a now dead controversy, in which these bottles were used as evidence of the manufacture of porcelain in China centuries before our era.

I

CERAMIC PROCESSES ILLUSTRATED

ATTENTION is drawn at this point to the series of twelve pictures, on the pillar between Bays XXIX and XXVIII, illustrating the processes of manufacture at Kingtehchen. Starting from the west side of the pillar (1) the top picture shows the workmen getting the clay from a pit in the hills and carrying it away in baskets slung on shoulder-poles. (2) In the next we see the china stone being crushed by pounders driven by a water-wheel; and (3) in the third the china clay is being beaten and kneaded to the required plasticity.

The two essential materials for the porcelain body are china clay (*kaolin*), an infusible substance which forms the solid part of the ware, and china stone (called *petuntse*), a fusible material, which forms the glassy element of the body and, softened by lime, the glaze. It has already been noted that other materials, such as steatite or pegmatite (*hua shih*) and *ch'ing tien* stone, were used in the composition of special bodies, and there were modifications also of the glaze; but the prime ingredients of the ordinary porcelain are *kaolin* and *petuntse*. Both of these were first obtained in the hills near Kingtehchen, but as the neighbouring deposits were exhausted it was necessary to obtain supplies from a distance of sixty or seventy miles. When the raw materials had been thoroughly purified and refined they were mixed into a plastic dough ready to be moulded into shape or 'thrown' on the potter's wheel.

(4) The fourth shows the potter 'throwing' the rounded wares on the wheel. In the case of wares decorated in underglaze colours such as blue and red, the next operation was painting on the raw body of the ware, after it had been dried. (5) This operation is shown in the fifth picture at the top of the south side of the pillar. (6) The next operation was the glazing, the liquid glaze being painted on with a brush, blown on through a tube or applied by immersing the vessel in a tub of glaze. The last method is the one illustrated. Passing to the east side of the pillar we see in picture (7) the kilns in which the porcelain was fired.

When this firing operation was finished, the porcelain, if it was of the blue and white variety, was complete. But if decoration in on-glaze enamels was to be added it went to the enamelling sheds.

In picture (8) the enamellers are seen painting the ware; and incidentally the grinding of the colours is also illustrated. In picture (9) we see the small 'muffle' kilns in which the ware, so painted, received its second baking at the moderate heat required to fuse the enamels.

A third baking, also in a muffle, was required if gilding or silvering was used. By these means the decoration in *famille verte* and *famille rose* enamels was accomplished. In some cases the porcelain received part of its decoration in underglaze blue and the remainder in enamels. Two square vases in Bay XXIX illustrate the stages of this process: in one the design is part-painted in blue only, and in the other it is finished with the overglaze enamels. Instances are known in which porcelain in a semi-decorated condition has been brought to Europe to be finished by European enamellers (see p. 123).

The remaining pictures (10 to 12) show the porcelain being packed in large circular cases at the factory, the transport of such cases overland on the poles of carriers, and finally the packing of large rectangular cases of porcelain for dispatch to Europe.

These pictures do not exhaust the processes of manufacture. Such operations for instance as making moulds, pressing the ware in moulds, carving and etching the designs, &c., are not illustrated; but what is shown serves admirably as a general introduction to the technique of Chinese porcelain.

FIG. 184. The Twin Genii of Union and Harmony. Tehwa. 17th century. L. 6 in.

PROVINCIAL PORCELAIN

PORCELAIN was made at several places besides Kingtehchen, but Chinese writers have little to say about it except that it was inferior to that of the Kiangsi factory. It is practically impossible to identify the wares made in the several provincial factories, with one exception—that of Tehwa (Tê-hua), which lies about seventy-five miles due north of Amoy in the province of Fukien. We know little of the story of the factories here. They are reputed to have been started in the Ming period, apparently towards the end of that dynasty; and an English missionary who visited them in 1880 found the industry in full activity.

From Chinese sources we learn that the Tehwa porcelain was at first very expensive to make, but that by the beginning of the eighteenth century it was very widely distributed and no longer dear.

The European traders at Amoy made the Tehwa porcelain

familiar in Europe in the latter part of the seventeenth and the early part of the eighteenth century, and much of it has been handed down under the French name of *blanc de chine*.

It is a fine white and highly vitrified porcelain, usually very translucent, and covered with a soft-looking, melting glaze which blends so closely with the body that it is difficult to find the dividing line between body and glaze. It is almost always white, sometimes milk white, sometimes creamy, and occasionally of ivory tint, faintly tinged with red; and the texture of the glaze can be compared with that of milk jelly or blancmange.

A good series of specimens in Bay XXVIII illustrates the prevailing types of ware produced; but as the nature of the material seems to have

Fig. 185. God of Wealth. Tehwa: dated 1610. H. 11 in.

been changed very little during the last three centuries, the dating of individual pieces is generally a difficult matter.

This consideration gives additional interest to two inscribed specimens in the collection. They are a water bowl, or mortar, of Fukien, if not actually of Tehwa, make, which has a date = A.D. 1511; and the figure (fig. 185) of 'the God of Wealth' which has an inscription incised under the glaze and including a date = A.D. 1610. For the rest a plain white cylindrical brush-pot or incense vase is possibly of Ming date, and one or two other specimens are attributed to that period on stylistic grounds. A little figure of a Dutch soldier in the same section was doubtless made about 1650, and its material is of the finest translucent cream-white variety. A taller figure of a European in the milky white variety of the ware can be dated from its costume about 1700. Other pieces can be safely assigned to the K'ang Hsi period from their forms, which were repeated in the earliest European porcelains.[1] A cylindrical mug, two globular mugs with straight, ribbed necks, and a plain coffee-cup have shapes which are found in European wares[2] of mid-K'ang Hsi date. The kettle with figures in relief in sunk panels, the vase with arched handle and prunus sprigs

FIG. 186.—Tehwa porcelain cup: about 1700. H. 2·25 in.

in relief, and the fruit-shaped teapot, are all types copied by European porcelain-makers in the early part of the eighteenth century. The teapot is one of the pieces recovered from the Dutch wrecks in Table Bay, as is also a horn-shaped libation cup.

It will be seen that the Fukien wares are chiefly of an ornamental kind: figures of deities and mortals, incense vases, libation cups (fig. 186), often of bronze and rhinoceros-horn shapes, boxes, writing-table accessories, and vases. The decoration is formed by moulding, application of reliefs, or incising; occasionally it is rather coarsely painted in *famille verte* enamels.

[1] The Fukien wares provided many models for the European manufacturers at Meissen, St. Cloud, Chantilly, Bow, Chelsea, &c.; and some of the artificial porcelains of Europe—particularly that of St. Cloud—have such a strong resemblance to the creamy type of Fukien that the two wares can easily be mistaken at a casual glance.

[2] Fukien specimens of this kind have been erroneously attributed to Tschirnhausen of Dresden and Dwight of Fulham. Examples of the shapes just described can be seen among the English stonewares in Bay XII, Case A, and it will be noticed that both the Chinese and English potters added a detached roll of clay below the base of the handles. This doubtless is the potter's version of the tail which completes the handle of silver mugs and cups.

The creamy white ware is seen at its best in a crab-shaped ornament, and the ivory type in the small figure of Bodhidharma (fig. 187).

Marks are not common, though apocryphal Ming date-marks occasionally appear, as also seals with potters' names such as Lai Kuan on a figure of Kuan Yin, and Ho Chao-tsung on the group of Twin Genii (fig. 184) from the Eumorfopoulos Collection.

Figs. 187 and 188. Tehwa porcelain, 17th century, figure of Bodhidharma; and bottle with dragon. H. 8 in.

A few more Fukien figures and groups are included in the porcelain showing European influences in Bay VI; and it is curious to note that in several cases the European figure is apparently credited with divine attributes. In one instance he takes the place of the Buddha in a shrine, and in another he is mounted on a kylin like one of the Arhats.

In Bay V will be seen a series of dishes which clearly belong to one family. Their provenance is uncertain but some southern Chinese pottery was probably responsible for them. Indeed, if we can trust the gossip of the antique trade, they were made in the neighbourhood of Swatow.

Their common features are a coarse porcelain body which burns reddish brown in the unglazed parts of the base, a greyish-white glaze sometimes crackled, and large accretions of sand and grit by the foot-rim—the remains of the material on which they were supported in the kiln. They are decorated in a free and perfunctory style by a variety of methods: with incised designs beneath a plain white glaze, with underglaze blue, with green, red, and turquoise-green enamels in late Ming style (fig. 189),

Fig. 189.   Dish with red and green enamels: export ware, about 1600.   D. 15·2 in.

and with white slip on grounds of celadon, brown, or blue glaze. Evidently made for the export trade, they are found in the East Indies, India, and Persia, and the date of their manufacture appears[1] to be the latter part of the sixteenth and the seventeenth centuries.

EUROPEAN INFLUENCES

BAY VI

REFERENCE has been made from time to time to European influences on the form and decoration of Chinese porcelain. They may be traced in ever-increasing volume from the late Ming period to the nineteenth century; and it has been considered worth while to illustrate this phase of Chinese ceramics by a special exhibition in Bay VI. Here we see Chinese porcelain decorated with European subjects and displaying European forms, Chinese porcelain decorated in China with designs (armo-

[1] The collection of dishes in the Bibi Maqbara at Aurangabad, which belonged to Aurangzeb and perhaps to Akbar, includes many specimens of this ware: and fragments of it were found on the site of Bijapur which was destroyed in 1686.

rial and otherwise) supplied directly by the European merchants, and, as a corollary, Chinese porcelain decorated in Europe by Europeans. A few specimens of Japanese porcelain are included. Many of the pieces are interesting for the light they throw on the relations between Chinese and Europeans in the early days of their intercourse, and many are important to the ceramic student because they can be dated with exactitude and consequently have documentary value.

The Fukien white figures and groups in Bay VI have already

Figs. 190, 191, and 192. Porcelain showing European influence; late 17th century. H. of figure 9 in.

been mentioned. A figure of a European lady in seventeenth-century dress (fig. 191) is evidently of early K'ang Hsi date, and a group of a man and woman near by belongs to the early part of the eighteenth century. The European trader was familiar to the Chinese of Canton and Amoy, but the potters of Kingtehchen and Tehwa were content with a very amateurish rendering of his features.

One of the earliest specimens in this section is a flattened bottle with blue and white ornament in transition style enclosing a drawing of a Spanish dollar; and with it may be ranked in date the vase and ewer described below. Close to it are two cups and a bowl of K'ang Hsi blue and white with a crucifix surrounded by Chinese ornament (fig. 192). Père d'Entrecolles, writing from Kingtehchen in 1712, says that such pieces were at one time made to order for the Christians in Japan, but that the traffic in such forbidden goods had been stopped some sixteen years before the time of writing. Later examples of this so-called 'Jesuit china' are decorated with sacred subjects frankly copied from European engravings. A series of plates alludes to the South Sea Bubble, and there are mugs and bowls with historic characters such as Prince Charles Edward, John Wilkes, and others. A few purely European shapes will be noticed, a candlestick or oil lamp, a *coupe trembleuse*, a vase of Italian form and another with masks obviously modelled on a piece of European (probably Dutch) faïence and a tall ewer. The two last appear to be late Ming or transition types. An extreme instance of the action and reaction of Chinese and European influences is the supper-set of trays copied in China, mark and all, from a Dutch Delft set which was itself obviously based on a Chinese prototype. A covered cup and saucer is similarly copied, mark and all, from a piece of French, St. Cloud, porcelain.

Of the large punch-bowls above the Pier-cases in Bays VI and XXIX two are painted with views of the river front of Canton with the 'hongs', or trading-stations, flying the flags of various European nations: two others with Chinese renderings of English agricultural scenes are inscribed 'W. E. S. Warren Lodge 1769' and 'J. C. Felden Farm 1779'.

The armorial porcelain in Bay VI illustrates European designs of a highly specialized kind. But it has much besides its heraldic interest to recommend it. Quite a number of the pieces can be accurately dated by the armorial bearings and others approximately; and as the coat of arms is usually supplemented by Chinese decorations of various kinds, often carefully painted in good colours, it is possible to form a useful chronological series of specimens in which the body, glaze, colours, and border designs in use at stated periods can be studied. The earliest example is a late Ming blue and white plate with a rough rendering of a shield of arms with helmet, crest and mantling. Armorial services were fashionable in the eighteenth century and drawings of arms and crests were sent out to China to be reproduced on the native porcelain. The actual porcelain was made at Kingtehchen and in the earlier days of this trade most of it was decorated there. This is evident from the colours, underglaze blue and *famille verte* enamels, the former of which could only have been applied at the place of manufacture, while the latter were not used, as far as we know, at any of the decorating establishments elsewhere in which the armorial porcelain was painted.

There are several examples of K'ang Hsi armorial to which this statement applies, one of them (by no means the earliest) dated 1702. But the orders were doubtless transmitted through Canton, where European trade was concentrated in the eighteenth century and, as the porcelain was also shipped from that town, it soon occurred to the Chinese that the orders for special decorations could be conveniently carried out in the workshops at Canton which were already engaged on the analogous work of painting on enamelled metal.[1]

Old bills for these services still exist to prove their origin, and attention is called to the photographs of two such documents relating to two services with the arms and crest of Peers shipped from Canton in 1731. A specimen of each of the services completes this useful exhibit, one painted in underglaze blue and the other in enamel colours. A plate inscribed on the back

Figs. 193 and 194. Armorial porcelain, K'ang Hsi period. D. 9·4 in.

Canton in China 24th Jany 1791 is further evidence of this traffic. Space does not permit us to set out in full all the lessons which can be learnt from the armorial series, but a few instances may be quoted to point the way to the student.[2]

One is a deep plate with inscription dated 1702. Apart from the coat of arms (of de Vassy of Holland) it is painted with floral designs in *famille verte* enamels in pure Chinese taste and it may be regarded as typical mid-K'ang Hsi work (fig. 193).

In the same Case there are five dishes which can be dated about 1720. They are partly decorated in underglaze blue and partly in *famille verte* enamels. The blue in most cases is of the pencilled kind, but the graded washes appear on at least one of the series.

A dated example of Yung Chêng *famille rose* is seen in a cup and saucer with the arms of the Dutch East India Company in

[1] See also p. 98.

[2] It is perhaps superfluous to add that none of the class of ware under discussion ever was, or could have been, made at the Lowestoft factory. The Lowestoft fallacy has been exposed so often that it can hardly have any further currency.

1728; and a richly painted plate with the Okeover arms (fig. 195) was supplied to the family of that name in 1743. The teapot[y] with arms of Maitland of Pitrichie (about 1740) is a specimen of the dead-white glassy porcelain previously mentioned, and it is also noticeable for its shape, which is clearly based on a Meissen model. There are twenty specimens in the Collection belonging to the Ch'ien Lung period which can be dated within a year or two and which range from 1740 to 1791; but it will be

FIG. 195. Plate with arms of Okeover, made in 1743. D. 8·9 in.

seen from these that the supplementary ornament becomes less and less Chinese as the century advances. The border patterns in use from time to time are worth noticing, as many of them appear on other wares besides the armorial. Finally, attention is drawn to a teapot which has a panel frame and border designs in underglaze blue. Its decoration has not been completed, and it was doubtless sent to Canton to be finished in enamels but was bought by some European merchant who had an order to get undecorated or partly decorated Chinese porcelain for a European enamelling establishment. A finished piece of a similar kind is illustrated by fig. 196.

The extent to which this kind of treatment was applied to Chinese and Japanese porcelain can be gauged from the group of plain white Fukien and Kingtehchen porcelain, white ware with engraved designs or sparsely decorated specimens, which have been coloured by European decorators. A plate with a picture of a ship is interesting as having the date 1700 on the vessel's stern. Some of the work is often a feeble imitation of

Oriental decoration (generally in the style of the Japanese Kakiemon ware) applied by Dutch enamellers. A bowl in the top section is painted with parrots in a manner which recalls the Dutch Delft brush-back in Case E of Bay XXIII. Other pieces are treated to European designs by accredited painters at Meissen, Bow, Chelsea, and elsewhere, and even transfer-printed

Figs. 196, 197, and 198. Vase with panels painted in Europe; clobbered bottle; jar painted in black and gold, perhaps by Preissler. H. 9·7 in.

at Worcester. Others again (fig. 198) have been decorated with great care and skill by the competent *chambrelans*, or private enamellers, in Germany such as the Preisslers in Silesia and Bohemia, and Bottengruber and von Wolfsburg in Breslau. Such pieces as these are highly prized to-day and have undoubted merit; but unfortunately the European enameller did not confine his attention to the undecorated ware. Indeed he did not hesitate to ruin many respectable specimens of Chinese blue and white and underglaze red by 'clobbering' them with clumsy additions in enamel colours (fig. 197). Less objectionable are one or two specimens with monochrome grounds which have been decorated in Europe with floral scrolls cut on the lapidary's wheel.

COREAN WARES

THE peninsula of Corea stretches out from Northern China towards the southernmost island of the Japanese group and forms a natural link between the two Empires, so that it is not surprising to find that the early tomb wares of Japan and Corea are almost identical in form and make, and that both reflect something of the burial customs of China. Such is the characteristic pottery of the pre-Silla[1] period, which forms one definite type of Corean ware. It is usually of a slaty grey colour varying from soft pottery to hard stoneware, and from a coarse, gritty material to a smooth, thin, and neatly finished ware. It is made on the wheel, and ornamented with wheel-rings, incised wavy patterns, and cross-hatching which suggests pressure of some coarse textile; but it is unglazed, except for accidental accretions of a greenish-brown smear formed by wood ashes in the kiln. The vessels include jars, libation cups, food bowls, &c., and they are often mounted on high stems perforated with slits or triangular openings. One or two specimens of this kind of ware are shown in Bay V, but the main collection is in reserve.[2] This type of pottery continued to be made during the Silla period but in more sophisticated forms (fig. 199), and side by side with glazed wares. Some of the Silla pottery has a greenish brown glaze rather like that of proto-porcelain (p. 9), and another kind with soft reddish buff body has a green lead glaze like that of the Chinese Han pottery.

In 918 the State of Koryu revolted against Silla and assumed the hegemony of Corea. Thus began the Koryu or Korai dynasty (918–1392), the most flourishing period of Corean art. The pottery of this period is known from the contents of tombs excavated around Song-do, the capital at this time, and much of it is very beautiful. It was, indeed, good enough to receive favourable notice from a Chinese writer in the twelfth century, who compares it with the celebrated *pi sê* ware of Yüeh Chou, the Ju ware, and the Ting. The Corean tomb wares in the Collection include: (1) white stoneware or porcelain with creamy glazes of Ting type; (2) a transparent porcelain of *ying ch'ing* type (see p. 36); (3) a grey porcellanous ware with celadon-green or bluish green glaze; and (4) a coarse brownish-grey ware with thin greyish glaze tending to brown and much affected by the colour

---

[1] Silla, one of the three ancient States of Corea, absorbed the others in the seventh century.

[2] It was mainly obtained from graves near Fusan, and, like the similar wares from Japanese dolmens, it was almost all collected by the late Mr. W. Gowland.

of the body beneath it. Specimens of the first two types are always liable to be claimed as Chinese, for it is certain that Chinese pottery was freely traded in Corea; and even the third type will in some cases be very difficult to distinguish from the Northern Chinese celadons and the Yüeh ware. But there are peculiarly Corean shapes and decorations which differentiate

FIG. 199. Food-vessel from a tomb at
Fusan: Silla period. H. 6·3 in.

the wares in many cases; and the Corean finish of the foot-rims is generally distinct from that of the Chinese, the hollow part of the base being very shallow and often slightly convex, covered with glaze, and showing the marks of 'spurs' or 'piles of sand' on which the vessels rested in the kiln. For the rest the Corean celadon glaze is usually more opaque and bluer than the Chinese, and the potting of the wares is less accurate.

The decoration includes incised, carved, and moulded designs closely following the Chinese Ting ware, and delicate inlaid designs in white and black clays which are essentially Corean. This last is called by the Japanese *mishima* decoration, because one favourite pattern recalled the lines of ideographs on the almanacs compiled at Mishima, in Japan. The typical *mishima* pattern with radiating lines and bands of small rosettes (fig. 201) in white is commonly seen on the fourth of the types described above, and this ware was freely imitated in Japan. Ware of this coarse greyish type, as well as some of the better kind, is sometimes painted in brown (fig. 203). This is the *e-gorai* (painted Corean) of the Japanese. Typical designs on the Koryu celadons are floral scrolls, boys holding branches (a Buddhistic motive) (fig. 205), ducks and water, lotus petals, &c., engraved or impressed in Ting style: and among the inlaid patterns we frequently see medallions with a stork in clouds, scrolls of vine or of daisy-like flowers (fig. 206), and small floral sprays, in addition to the characteristic 'corduroy' patterns.

Fig. 200. Vase. H. 9·6 in. Fig. 201. *Mishima* bowl.
Fig. 202. Typical Corean ewer: Koryu period.

The Koryu dynasty was followed by the dynasty of Yi, which lasted from 1392 to 1910. The capital was now removed to Seoul, the name of the kingdom was changed to Chosen, and Buddhism was replaced by Confucianism. At the end of the sixteenth century the Japanese invasion under Hideyoshi ruined what prosperity was left to Corea; and after this time the country was virtually closed to the outside world, becoming in fact the 'Hermit Kingdom'.

The pottery of the Yi period has none of the distinction of the Koryu ware; and it would seem that, when the capital was moved from Song-do, the potting industry there was left to decay. The Yi wares are best known to us by the Japanese imitations, among which we recognize a pottery with red or brownish-grey body and translucent glaze varying from brown to light grey

FIG. 203. Painted Corean (*e-gorai*) vase. Koryu period. H. 12 in.

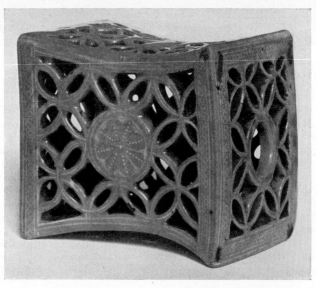

FIG. 204. Head-rest. Koryu period. L. 4·9 in.

FIG. 205. Bowl with boys and foliage in
moulded relief. D. 6·9 in.

FIG. 206. Vase with black and white
mishima inlay. H. 13·5 in.

tinged with pink; brown-painted wares; coarse *mishima* ware; a coarse ware with creamy-buff glaze minutely crackled (the forerunner of the Satsuma faïence); and a grey ware with opaque

Fig. 207. Cup-stand with incised ornament. D. 5 in.

Fig. 208. Vase with underglaze blue and red
designs: about 1600. H. 13·6 in.

milk-white glaze, thin, and resembling a wash of paint: both these last types are known as *koma-gai* (white Corean).

The later Corean wares in the Collection, which are by no means representative, include a few with black and *flambé* glazes, a crackled grey or buff porcelain of coarse texture with or without sketchy designs in dull underglaze blue, porcelain painted in underglaze blue and red (fig. 208), and white porcelain with reliefs and sometimes openwork.

SIAMESE WARES

(BAY VI, CASES A, B, TABLE-CASE and WINDOW-CASE)

It is difficult to obtain exact information about the early history of Siam and still more so about its pottery;[1] but it is believed that the old capitals, Sawankhalok, Sukhothai, and Ayuthia, all had their potteries; and it is stated that the industry lasted at Ayuthia down to the destruction of the city in 1767. There is tangible evidence of the industry at old Sawankhalok, which was situated near the modern town of the same name on the Me Nam River about 200 miles N. of Bangkok; for the sites of ruined potteries have been excavated there by Mr. Lyle[1] and others, two groups of kilns being found buried beneath mounds of earth. In one group, the more northerly, there were, according to Lyle,[2] about fifty mounds; and the better, and probably earlier, class of ware was recovered from this site. In the other group, about three miles distant, a variety of coarser wares were unearthed. Tradition asserts that the industry was started with Chinese help at a very early date, and the character of the ware certainly points to a Chinese origin. At the same time it suggests a date somewhere in the Sung period, say twelfth or thirteenth century, as the *terminus a quo*. Again we have only local tradition and the style of the ware to guide us in estimating the duration of the Sawankhalok potteries.[2] Some accounts make it last down to the eighteenth century, and we might at any rate put it as late as the seventeenth on stylistic grounds.

A representative series from the Sawankhalok kilns is exhibited in Case A and in the Table-case of Bay VI. The most characteristic ware is a celadon type, with body varying from light grey stoneware to a white semi-porcelain (both burn a reddish colour in the unglazed parts) and a translucent glaze of greenish tone, occasionally a full celadon green but more often a watery grey green. The glaze has a tendency to run into pools at the bottom of bowls and dishes, and here it curdles and becomes flecked and streaked with milky grey shot with blue. Irregular, and evidently accidental, crackle is a common feature. The ornament of this

---

[1] See (a) Col. G. E. Gerini, 'Siamese Archaeology', *Journal of the Royal Asiatic Society*, April 1904; and the *Kingdom of Siam*, Louisiana Purchase Exposition, St. Louis, 1904; and (b) T. H. Lyle and C. H. Read, 'Notes on the Ancient Pottery Kilns of Sawankhalok', *Journal of the Royal Anthropological Institute*, new series, vol. vi, 1903, p. 238; and Reginald le May, 'The Ceramic Wares of North-Central Siam', in the *Burlington Magazine*, October and November 1933.

[2] Le May, op. cit., more precisely places the sites of the kilns at (1) Chaliang, one mile from the north entrance of the old city, and (2) Turiang, about four miles farther north. He considers 1300–1600 to be about the period covered by the industry at Sawankhalok.

ware generally consists of engraved rosettes and petalled bands, shaded at times with combed lines; wheel-made rings deeply cut on the shoulders of jars; channelled flutings on the exterior of bowls; and roughly scored lines. The forms of the ware are utilitarian—bowls, dishes, bottles, ewers, and jars—a common form of bottle having a globular body and small narrow neck with two loop-handles for a cord; and a peculiar feature of the finish is a roughly impressed ring on the base which is unglazed.

SAWANKHALOK WARE
FIG. 209. Bowl painted in brown: 17th century.
FIG. 210. Fluted jar. H. 3·2 in.

This ring is the imprint of the tubular support on which the ware was balanced in the kiln. Some of the bowls have also spur-marks inside, showing that in some cases they were piled, one inside the other, for firing. This is the typical ware (fig. 210) of the Northern series of kilns, and most of it probably dates back to the early period—say thirteenth to fifteenth century.

Other types, mostly[1] found in the Southern kilns, have the grey stoneware body with opaque greyish-white glaze, or a treacly-brown glaze (fig. 211), sometimes thin and translucent, sometimes running in thick drops, and very similar to that of some old Japanese tea-jars; painted designs in brown under a translucent greyish glaze (fig. 209); or no glaze at all.

[1] Wasters prove that in some instances the brown-glazed and the celadon wares were fired together, as also the brown-glazed and the brown-painted wares.

Many of the brown-painted wares may well be of sixteenth- and seventeenth-century dates, judging from the style of ornament; and they are the prototype of the Japanese *sunkoroku* ware of Satsuma (q.v.).

Tiles and bricks with relief designs and figures roughly modelled in the round were made in the grey and brown wares of the Southern kilns.

Sawankhalok wares, especially the celadons, are found in the

FIG. 211. Brown-glazed Sawan-khalok jar. H. 3·2 in.

FIG. 212. Chinese porcelain enamelled in Siamese taste. H. 8·2 in.

Philippine Islands,[1] in Borneo and other islands of the East Indian Archipelago, in India, Persia, and Egypt. They were perhaps shipped at Martaban[2] in Pegu, an entrepôt of medieval trade.

White porcelain proper does not seem to have been made in Siam, and the specimens in Bay VI, though found in Siam, are evidently of Chinese origin. They are mostly coarse wares and probably made in some Southern Chinese factory for export to Siam, for their forms—e.g. cinerary urns with pagoda-shaped knobs on their covers—and their enamelled decoration—e.g. Siamese Buddhistic figures, such as the taypanom (praying figure) and Norassing (half man and half horse), and much of the formal ornament—are in peculiarly Siamese taste (fig. 212).

[1] Manuscript notes on Sawankhalok wares in the Philippines by Dr. H. Otley Beyer are freely quoted by le May, op. cit.

[2] *Martabani* is one of the names, current in the Near East, for Chinese celadons. It is probably derived from the name of this port and applied to the Siamese as well as the Chinese wares.

There are similar objects, too, in coarse pottery which is also of Chinese origin.

A very large trade in pottery has been carried on since the Sung dynasty between Southern Chinese ports and the East Indies, India, and still farther west; and special types of ware and decoration were made for this market.

A few specimens from Borneo and India are shown in Bay VI; and there are a few specimens, of various dates, from Cambodia and Annam. They help to link up the Siamese and Chinese pottery, but they are by no means representative of the ceramics of Indo-China.

JAPANESE POTTERY

(*BAY VII*)

JAPAN like every other country has its primitive pottery. One type is a rough hand-made material, known as *kameoka* from the name of the region in which it is most plentifully found. Another and considerably more advanced type belongs to the dolmen[1] period which may be said to extend from the third century B.C. to the seventh century A.D. The dolmen-building people were invaders who came from the mainland, doubtless from Corea. Their burial customs were those of the Chinese and Coreans, and they placed in their tombs both human and animal figures modelled in clay, and a large assortment of pottery vessels. The finer pottery (fig. 232) is almost exactly the same as that made in the early periods in Corea. Some of it is a red hand-made ware; but the bulk of it is a slaty-grey ware of varying hardness, made, and sometimes slightly ornamented, on the wheel, and occasionally showing patches of hard brown glaze which was probably formed accidentally by alkali from the wood-ashes in the kiln.

In the eighth century A.D. a Chinese Buddhist priest, named Gyogi, is said to have come to Japan from Corea and to have travelled round the country giving instruction in the potter's art. Among other things he is reputed to have introduced the use of the potter's wheel, but the dolmen pottery proves that this instrument was already known. As might be expected, any primitive wheel-made pot dug up in Japan is apt to be called Gyogi's ware. The introduction of glaze is not included in the Gyogi tradition, but there is evidence that it was used at any rate on tiles of Japanese make about his time.

The historic collection at Nara, which was formed in the eighth century, tells us little as the pieces of pottery included in it are mostly Chinese; and there is no doubt that the island people

---

[1] A dolmen is a burial chamber formed by a single cap-stone supported by uprights. Those in Japan and Corea are covered by mounds of earth.

lagged far behind their great neighbours in the ceramic industry. In the thirteenth century, however, two events conspired to give the much-needed stimulus. One was the spread of tea-drinking[1] among the Japanese and the other was the visit of Kato Shiro-zaemon to China to study Chinese methods. Hitherto the Japanese seem to have depended on Corea for their inspiration, and Kato's visit marks an epoch in their ceramic history. On his return he worked at first with Chinese materials, making little tea-jars and other objects with thick glazes of the *temmoku* type (p. 30). In 1227 he found suitable clays at Seto, in the province of Owari; and there he settled and was succeeded by many generations of descendants. Kato Shirozaemon is generally known by the abbreviated name of Toshiro. The Seto wares will be described later.

Very little is known of medieval Japanese pottery, but we hear of factories founded in the eighth, ninth, eleventh, thirteenth, and fourteenth centuries for the most part by Coreans or under Corean influence, respectively at Shidoro, Takatori, Karatsu, Shigaraki, Iga, and Bizen, all names of potteries celebrated in the later periods. So far as is known, however, no well-glazed wares were made at any of these potteries, except perhaps at Karatsu, until the late thirteenth or early fourteenth century, nor was pottery of any distinction turned out at Shidoro, Taka-tori, or Iga until towards the end of the sixteenth century, when tea-utensils were made to the order of the tea-master Kobori Enshiu. It should be remembered, too, that lacquer was very largely used in Japan for domestic purposes, and that only simple unglazed wares were employed in the Shinto ritual, and these circumstances must have had a retarding effect on the development of pottery.

In any case it does not appear that really rapid progress was made till the end of the sixteenth century, when a number of highly skilled Corean potters were brought back in the wake of Hideyoshi's armies from Corea and settled in various parts of Japan. The potteries of Satsuma, Karatsu, Hagi, Takatori, Yatsushiro, and Kioto benefited from this immigration. More-over, about the same period, the famous tea-master Sen no Rikiu reorganized the tea ceremony (*cha no yu*), which from the time of its founder Shuko, during the shogunate of Yoshimasa (1449–90), has played a very important part in Japanese culture; and although its history belongs rather to sociology than to ceramics, its influence both in bringing the potter in personal contact with the educated public and in awakening an intelligent interest in the potter's art cannot be overestimated. A lacquered wooden figure of Rikiu is exhibited at the end of the Table-case in

---

[1] The cultivation of tea is said to have been known in Japan as early as A.D. 805, but it was not firmly established till later.

Bay VII, surrounded by some of the vessels and implements used in the ceremonial drinking of tea. Pottery vessels used for this purpose include the small jar to hold the powdered tea, the drinking-bowl, the washing-bowl and the cake-dish, and usually the water-holder, the incense-box, the incense-burner, the fire-holder, and a vase to hold a single spray of blossom which stood, or was suspended, in the niche (*toko*). The utmost simplicity and austerity were affected in the furniture of the room and in the utensils used, and ancient or primitive-looking pottery even of provincial origin, provided that it had an intrinsic merit of its own or was distinguished by well-attested historic associations, was no less a source of pride to its owner than the work of great potter artists, such as the early Raku masters, Koetsu or Kenzan. Indeed from the time of Nobunaga (1534–82) onwards, when the enthusiasm for the tea ceremony was at its height, the most appropriate (if not always best appreciated) gift that a prince could present to a retainer as a reward for military success was a tea-utensil of historic interest. These treasured vessels were kept in brocade bags in plain wooden boxes, made precious, perhaps, by an inscription in some historic calligraphy.

The old *cha no yu* pottery is very highly valued to-day, but it is not regarded as complete without its original silk wrappings and boxes. The fashion set by the tea ceremonies pervaded the life of the educated classes and at its best was a potent influence on the potter's art. On the other hand, during the period of sophistication which set in towards the beginning of the seventeenth century, the great manipulative skill of the Japanese potter was often masked by a studied roughness in the appearance of the wares, which after being accurately thrown on the wheel were deliberately made asymmetrical.[1] Again, the exterior of the ware is often left untrimmed, and a thick treacly glaze, running in drops and ending abruptly before reaching the base, is preferred to a smooth surface and fine finish. But these peculiarities are not necessarily affectations, for the contrast between the smooth lustrous glaze and the dull rough body has aesthetic value, and a thick, running glaze of the *temmoku* type, if allowed to overrun the foot, might cause the pot to adhere to the seggar with disastrous results.

Though quite a large proportion of the older Japanese pottery is obviously under the archaizing influence of the tea ceremony, there are still many types of ware in which fineness of finish was not consciously avoided. The stoneware with creamy, crackled glaze made at Satsuma and Kioto from the eighteenth century onwards and painted with designs in enamel colours and gilding

[1] This affectation was largely due to the influence of Kobori Enshiu, who is held by the more orthodox to have debased the tea ceremony. The same can also be said of Furuta Oribe.

PLATE XVIII

Fig. 213. Bizen stoneware figure of Hotei. H. 31 in.

leaves nothing to be desired in this respect. Moreover, the vast quantities of pottery and porcelain made, since the opening up of Japan in 1859, with an eye to foreign trade conform in general to European ideas.

The Japanese potters did not work in great organized centres like those at Kingtehchen in China. There were doubtless many potteries clustered together at Kioto and elsewhere, but the individual factories were usually small concerns run by one or two potters, or by a family. Hence the great variety and individuality of the wares and the numerous marks and signatures which appear on them.

It will be convenient to consider the different groups of wares in the order of their arrangement in the Cases of Bay VII.

Karatsu, in the province of Hizen, on the Island of Kiushiu, has been noted for pottery since the eleventh century when Corean settlers made there the first glazed ware of Japan. Corean potters were again brought to the district in the sixteenth century by Hideyoshi's orders. The commonest type of Karatsu ware is pottery of dark and fairly fine clay, over which is run a thick buff glaze, coarsely crackled, and generally with irregular patches of white towards the edge. From the early part of the seventeenth century grey or brownish wares, with brown designs painted in iron pigment under the glaze (fig. 214), were made in the style of the similarly decorated Corean ware (*e gorai*); besides which decoration with inlay in white or black slip in Corean style, or with coarse brush-marks (*hakeme*) in white slip, was freely used. Some of the archaic-looking pieces have a rough, blistered body, due to overfiring, and grey glaze which runs into drops like candle grease.

Satsuma[1] is probably the most familiar to Western ears of all the names of Japanese potteries, but it is almost entirely associated with the modern enamelled wares made for the European market. A better, but still very imperfect, idea of the Satsuma wares will be got from the specimens exhibited in Bay VII.

Satsuma is a princedom in the southern part of the Island of Kiushiu. Its potteries were of little account till 1596 when Shimazu, the prince of Satsuma, brought back from Corea a number of skilled potters who apparently settled in two divisions, one at Chosa and the other at Sasshiu.

The Chosa potters at first followed the Corean methods, making brownish or reddish-brown ware with translucent glaze and inlaid (*mishima*) decoration; but, perhaps influenced by the prince's collection of Chinese wares, Hochiu, the most noted potter of this group, made a new departure, producing a number

[1] An important article on 'The Potters and Pottery of Satsuma', by William L. Schwartz, is published in the *Transactions of the Japan Society*, London, vol. xix.

of novel glazes, among which may be mentioned a thick grey or brown, shrivelled into distinct globules which are compared with dragon scales (*ja katsu*); *flambé*, with greenish-blue markings like the Kwangtung stoneware (*namako*); iron-rust glaze (*tessha*), usually with splashes of *flambé*; black (*kuro*); black with gold specks; tea-green over russet-brown or pear-skin; mixed glazes— tea-green, greyish white, and rich brown; and tortoise-shell (*bekko*).

Fig. 214. Karatsu vase with prunus in brown. H. 9·8 in.
Fig. 215. Shino tray painted in blue: 17th century.

The potters of the Chosa group set up kilns in several districts, and, after many moves, the principal members united at Tatsu-monji in 1650. Painting in iron and cobalt oxide pigments (brown and blue) was introduced here in the third quarter of the seventeenth century, but most of the ware was plain until the characteristic Satsuma decoration in enamel colours was adopted in 1795. About this time a potter named Hoko, after a prolonged study at the principal potteries of Japan, introduced many new varieties of ware, and a great expansion of the industry took place. An attempt to make porcelain in this district in the seventeenth century proved abortive, and it was not renewed till late in the nineteenth century.

Meanwhile the other division of the Coreans set up kilns in the districts of Nawashiro and Kagoshima. In the former place a creamy crackled ware was made which is the forerunner of the fine Satsuma faïence. It is said to have been based on the *koma-gai*, a Corean ware of the Ting yao (see p. 31) type, and it certainly has some of the character of the *t'u ting* or earthy Ting ware. At the Tadeno factory, in Kagoshima, wares like Hochiu's were made; but it was here that the crackled ivory-white Satsuma faïence was first decorated in enamels and gold with brocade patterns (*nishiki de*). This kind of decoration came into use about

SATSUMA POTTERY

FIGS. 216 and 217. Black-glazed bottle; 17th century; and dragon-skin bowl (D. 8·7 in.).

1795 and was greatly developed in the nineteenth century. The early pieces are sparingly coloured and much play is made with the beautiful ivory-white, crackled surface. Later, the enamelled designs became more elaborate, and quantities of over-decorated wares were made for the European market at the end of the nineteenth century. This type has been freely imitated at Kioto, Ota, and elsewhere; and much of the so-called Satsuma is modern Kioto ware, painted in the enamelling establishments at Tokio. A superior imitation is made at the Meizan factory at Ozaka.

The Collection includes specimens of most of the Hochiu types—the dragon-skin;[1] black and brown glazes of Chinese *temmoku*[2] type (figs. 216, 217); the iron-rust brown with splashes

[1] Another variety of this shrivelled glaze, with slightly smaller granulations, is known as *same-yaki* (shark-skin ware). It appears in various colours and there are brown and grey specimens in the Collection.

[2] See p. 30.

of grey *flambé* which recall some of our T'ang wares; and the
tortoise-shell which is like the Chinese 'egg and spinach' glaze
(fig. 218). There are also tea-jars (fig. 219) with olive-brown
glaze, and it will be noticed on some of these that the thread-
marks[1] under the base trend from left to right, which is the
result of the Corean practice of turning the wheel with the left
foot. And there is a grey ware painted with formal designs in
brown (iron pigment) under the glaze (fig. 221), which has a

FIG. 218. Satsuma plate with *bekko*
glaze. D. 7·9 in.

FIG. 219. Satsuma tea-jar with
splashed glazes. H. 2·4 in.

strong resemblance to some of the Sawankhalok pottery (see
p. 133). It is in fact called *sunkoroku*, a Japanese rendering of
Sawankhalok. Examples of enamelled Satsuma are shown in the
Table-case.

Shigaraki ware was made in the village of Nagano-mura,
province of Omi, in the Island of Hondo. A coarse pottery was
made here in the thirteenth century; and in the sixteenth and
seventeenth centuries various *cha jin*, masters of the tea ceremony,
interested themselves in different kinds of Shigaraki ware, and
their names are now attached to the several types, viz. Sho-o
Shigaraki, a hard greyish buff ware with red-brown smear and
a little grey-green verdigris-coloured glaze; Rikiu Shigaraki, a
ware like the greyish crackled Corean pottery; Soton Shigaraki,

---

[1] Thread-marks (*itokiri*) are the concentric lines under the base made when
the piece is cut, with a piece of string or wire, from its bed on the wheel. As
a rule they trend from right to left.

with white body and crackled buff glaze; Enshiu Shigaraki, with mahogany-brown glaze.

Shigaraki ware is often confused with that of the neighbouring province of Iga, and there are two vases of Iga ware with the Shigaraki specimens.

Takatori ware was made in the province of Chikuzen, in the Island of Kiushiu. Two Coreans were brought over by the feudal chief, Kuroda, in the sixteenth century and settled at Takatori,

FIGS. 220 and 221. Satsuma bowl, grey with brown edging;
and *sunkoroku* tea-jar (H. 3·4 in.).

where they worked at first in Corean style and with Corean materials. The pottery was patronized by Kobori Enshiu, the famous tea-master and dilettante, in the seventeenth century; and a Hizen potter was associated with the management. Multiple glazes of the Seto type and *flambé* glazes were now introduced and became the characteristic feature of Takatori ware. The kilns were frequently moved in search of suitable clay, but they were apparently established in 1708 at Shikaharamura. The ware, as might be expected, varies in colour, being first grey, then nearly white, and then reddish or purplish; and the glazes are mainly coffee- or chocolate-brown, tea-dust green, rich purplish black or brown, and bluish grey *flambé*, besides the ordinary translucent brown and greenish brown. There are several kilns still at work, and some of these specialize in the old Takatori types of ware. Examples of Takatori vases (fig. 222) and tea-jars and a few dishes of the ware are shown. The tray (fig. 223) in form of a bamboo shoot illustrates the Japanese potter's fondness for copying natural forms, which is noticeable in other objects in the form of a peach, a shell, a fish, a bird, &c.

There have been many noted potteries in the province of Owari, in southern Hondo, the most important being at *Seto* where Kato Shirozaemon settled in 1227, after his visit to China. His first wares, made with Chinese materials, are known as *karamono*. Four generations of his family are celebrated in Japanese

Figs. 222 and 223. Takatori vase, brown with green splash; and tray in form of a bamboo shoot, marked *Ki* (L. 9·3 in.).

annals under the name of Toshiro I, Toshiro II, &c., but the family continued to manufacture for many generations further. Many different varieties of ware have been made in Seto as elsewhere in the province of Owari; the most characteristic, however, has a brown or grey body and either a *temmoku* brown, or an opaque yellowish-white crackled felspathic glaze, with designs painted in iron or copper oxide much in the manner of Oribe ware (p. 144), which has been made in the same province since the early seventeenth century. The glazes used by the Toshiros and their successors for tea ceremony pottery were of the *temmoku* variety, thick and semi-transparent, but coloured often to opacity by the presence of iron oxide. This oxide, whether added to the glaze or an original ingredient of the red clay and wood-ash used in its composition, presents, sometimes in streaks and flecks, sometimes in solid tints, all the varieties of subdued colour, ranging from whitish yellow through many different shades of brown, russet, and claret to black and even a dull silver, metallic blue or green, which are to be found in the various compounds of iron in their natural state. The second Toshiro is reputed to have invented the crackled yellow glaze known as *ki* (or yellow) Seto (fig. 224). Similar glazes to those of Seto were made in other potteries, the only differences being due to variations in

Fig. 224. Ki-Seto tea-jar, with yellow glaze. Fig. 225. Seto tea-jar.
H. 4·2 in. Fig. 226. Zeze (Seta ware) tea-jar with splashed brown glaze.

the nature of the clay and wood-ash employed, and in later times, when a greater number of ingredients were used, to slight differences in the formulae. Factory marks do not seem to have been used on Seto pottery until the nineteenth century, although the personal marks of individual potters occur as early as the second half of the sixteenth century, when six of the best of the Seto potters were distinguished by Nobunaga, and ten others were ordered to make utensils for the tea ceremony by Furuta Oribe in 1585.

The specimens in Bay VII give a good idea of the tea-ware with Seto glazes of various kinds. Some of the pieces are reputed to be of early date—*karamono*, *ki-seto*, and the like—but as we know that tea-ware almost identical in form and glaze was made not only in Seto but elsewhere in Owari from the thirteenth or fourteenth until well into the seventeenth century, and that most of the forms have persisted until the present day, the attribution of very early examples, especially to individual potters such as the Toshiros, of whose methods of work and output practically nothing is known, is a matter mainly of conjecture. There is less difficulty in distinguishing between the simple earlier pieces, which were as a rule glazed both inside and outside, and the sophisticated work made from the late sixteenth century onwards as well as the tea-ware produced from the early seventeenth century on under tea-master influence at other centres, such as Takatori, Zeze, Iga, Shidoro, Satsuma or Tamba, for

FIG. 227. Owari bowl (*Ofuke* ware) with green and
red splashes. D. 7·2 in.

the reason that each of these wares has a distinct character of its own.

The other Owari factories represented are (1) *Narumi*. Furuta Oribe started a factory here at the end of the sixteenth century, and the name Oribe ware is general for all the Narumi wares which are made to this day. The glazes are sugary white, orange-red, sage-green, salmon-pink, brown and black, alone or combined; and sketchy painted designs are often added in brown iron pigment and white slip. (2) *Akazu*, near Nagoya, established in the seventeenth century. Its wares are of the Seto type; but the potters were taken about 1630 by the prince of Owari for a private kiln close to his castle at Nagoya, and the wares made here are called *Ofuke* or, more rarely, *Oniwa* wares. The most characteristic Ofuke ware has a 'vitreous, semi-translucent glaze, over which are run broad bands of brown ochre, splashed with a glaze like aventurine lacquer, and between the bands are streaks of green and violet'. Specimens of this type are shown.

Another seventeenth-century Akazu pottery was the *Shuntai* ware. It had a variegated glaze usually 'grey crackle streaked with blue showing shades of violet and buff'.

A nineteenth-century potter, named Toyosuke, of Nagoya, made pottery bowls, &c., with greenish-grey glaze, painted inside in black and green and lacquered with black and gold, &c., on the exterior; it is often marked *Ho-raku*, from the name of the factory.

(3) A factory started near the castle of *Inuyama* in 1752 and moved in 1830 to *Maruyama*, made a grey stoneware with colourless translucent glaze painted, commonly with designs of maple leaves, in red brown, russet red, and green with black lines and white slip. A plate in the Collection illustrates the ware; it is marked *inu-yama*, which has the same characters as the name of the famous potter Kenzan (q.v.).

FIG. 228. Tea-bowl with mark, *Soma*. H. 3 in.

There are a few specimens of *Shino* ware on exhibition. It is a Seto ware with thick crackled white and grey glazes, often painted with impressionistic designs especially of grasses and blossoms in iron brown or cobalt blue (fig. 215). It takes its name from the *cha jin* Shino Ienobu (*fl.* 1480), and all Seto ware of this kind was subsequently called Shino. Other interesting Seto specimens are the bowls which imitate the Chinese Chien ware (q.v.).

Soma ware was made at a factory started by a retainer of the prince of Soma, at Nakamura, province of Iwaki, in south-west Hondo, in 1655. The manufacture continues to the present day. The characteristic Soma ware is a grey stoneware: (1) without glaze or with only a smear; (2) with brown specks and a translucent glaze (fig. 228). The cups and bowls usually have indentations in the sides and the favourite ornaments are the devices of Soma, a tethered horse—in brown, blue, or white slip in slight relief—or, more rarely, the nine balls. Other varieties have splashes of *flambé* glaze, red streaked with blue grey, purplish blue, brown, green, &c.; marbled brown and grey; and granulated glaze like the *same-yaki*[1] or shark-skin ware.

A brown-specked grey ware very similar to that of Soma was made at Maiko in the province of Harima in the nineteenth century.

The neighbouring exhibits include specimens of Iga, Zeze, Tamba, Shidoro, Hagi, Akahada, and Idsumo wares. The *Iga*

[1] *Yaki* is the Japanese equivalent of the Chinese *yao* (kiln or ware).

wares made at Marubashira, province of Iga, in Hondo, resemble the Seto and Shigaraki types. The older *Zeze* (province of Omi) wares of the seventeenth century were in the Seto and Takatori styles; the more modern include a cream-glazed ware in the Awata style (q.v.). Seta ware (fig. 226) is one of the old Zeze types. *Shidoro* (province of Totomi) wares are of a similar nature, but some of them were in Bizen style (q.v.): the Seto influence was strong in the seventeenth century. *Tamba* (near Kioto)

FIG. 229. Odo incense-vase, with black and white inlay. H. 6 in.

produced tea vessels with mahogany glazes, &c., in Seto fashion in the seventeenth century: the few specimens in the Collection are mainly of fine red stoneware with dull black or brown glaze splashed with coffee-brown and purplish black. The wares made at *Hagi*, province of Nagato, from the sixteenth century onwards have some novel features. The industry was started by Rikei, a Corean brought over by the prince of Choshiu. He made ware with a greyish crackled glaze clouded with salmon-pink, and distinguished by a nick in the foot-rim. A factory was opened by another expert at Matsumoto in the seventeenth century. The Hagi ware is mostly red-brown in body with soft pinkish grey glaze; but there are besides lavender glazes evidently based on the Chinese Chün types,[1] *flambé* grey shot with blue, cream-white, and brown-painted.

Another ware with greyish pink glaze of Hagi type is called *Akahada* from a hill by the town of Gojo in the province of Yamato. It ranges in date from the seventeenth century to the present day, and the factory mark is *Akahada* in a gourd- or kidney-shaped stamp.

Another Hagi-like ware was made in *Idsumo*. Indeed it is said to have been first made with materials from Hagi in the second half of the seventeenth century. Other Idsumo wares have glazes of Seto type: 'aventurine' glaze; soft wax-like yellow glaze decorated in gold, red, and green; and elaborate ornament in enamel colours on a greyish ware.

Odo ware was made at Otsu, near Kochi, the capital of Tosa in southern Hondo. The factory was started by a Corean named

Shohaku at the end of the sixteenth century, and Brinkley[1] describes the early wares as of light red clay with diaphanous glaze and a white glaze (or slip) used as a covering or 'like streaks of snow'.

The specimens shown have lustrous grey glaze over incised ornament filled with slip (fig. 229), painting in brown and black, and green or green and yellow glazes, and enamelling in Ninsei style (q.v.).

Three tea-bowls represent the *Asahi* ware which was first made

FIG. 230. Ko-Banko incense-vase: painted in red and green. H. 3·5 in.

at Uji, in Yamashiro, in the seventeenth century. Two have a buff body with crackled pinkish grey glaze, and the third has a brownish body with sparse and uneven grey glaze (in Corean style) and a nick in the foot-rim. The pottery is continued to-day by the family of Matsubayashi, and the present representative of this family assigned the two first of the above bowls to the early period and the third to Chobei Matsubayashi (1830–73). The mark used reads *asa-hi* (morning light).

Yedo, or Tokio, the capital of Japan, is represented by the *Imado* wares which include several unglazed fire-holders of soft-looking black or marbled pottery with polished surface, an interesting jar or fire-bowl of Raku type painted in green and red, and a large vase standing on a pedestal; a bowl of *Sumidagawa*[2] ware with soft reddish yellow glaze of Raku type; a covered box of brown unglazed pottery resembling carved wood, which was made by a lady potter named *Koren*; and possibly

[1] *Japan, Its History, Arts, and Literature*, vol. viii, p. 348.
[2] So called because the pottery was situated on the Sumida River.

a tea-bowl with the Kenzan mark, painted with plum blossoms in Kenzan style. Three interesting bowls (fig. 231) from the Sloane Collection, which, in spite of their fresh appearance, have been in the Museum since 1753, have been variously attributed to Odo and Yatsushiro; but a dish of similar ware in the Imperial Household Museum, Ueno Park, Tokio, is labelled Utsu-tsu-gawa ware, Yedo.

Two shelves are occupied by a variety of *Banko* wares. Banko is a name taken by a clever amateur potter who lived at Kuwana, province of Ise, from 1736 to 1795: he copied Raku, Corean, Ninsei, and Kenzan wares, besides doing original work. In 1786

Fig. 231.   Tea-bowl: perhaps Utsu-tsu-gawa
ware; Sloane Coll. D. 4·2 in.

he was invited to Yedo and settled for a time at Komme-mura. He learnt Chinese methods of enamelling and copied the late Ming 'red and green family'. His ware is the ko-Banko (old Banko) and his marks are *banko* and *fuyeki*. A probable specimen of the ko-Banko is the hexagonal incense vessel (fig. 230) which is painted in red and green enamels with diaper patterns.

About 1830 a potter, named Mori Yusetsu, accidentally came into possession of Banko's recipes and revived the Banko ware at Kuwana. He was a clever potter and not merely an imitator. He introduced the use of interior moulds and made a specialty of thin, cleverly moulded wares which show the marks caused by pressure of the potter's fingers on the exterior. Yusetsu obtained the original Banko seal and used it on his wares. The Banko types were taken up by numerous potters in the last half of the nineteenth century at Yokkaichi, the seaport of Kuwana.

Among the Banko wares in the Collection are ivory-white porcelain, white pottery with crackled glaze, light buff stoneware with grey glaze, soft buff pottery with crackled yellow glaze, greyish pottery with translucent crackled glaze painted in under-glaze blue and enamels, biscuit ware with thick opaque enamels,

and unglazed teapots pressed on exterior moulds. These last
are made of white, grey, brown, and marbled stonewares, thin
enough to be translucent, and ornamented with applied, pierced,
engraved, stamped, and enamelled designs.

A less definite group includes imitations of the grey and white
Corean wares,[1] plain and with incised designs and inlaid *mishima*
decoration; an archaic-looking flask, from the Ninagawa Col-

FIG. 232. Vase from a Japanese   FIG. 233. Bottle with splashed glaze in
    dolmen. H. 11·5 in.   T'ang style. H. 7·5 in.

lection, reputed to have been made 'in Japan under instruction
from a Corean potter, about A.D. 200'; a vase from the Gowland
Collection of dolmen pottery (fig. 232), and a bottle-shaped flask
of buff stoneware with mottled brownish yellow glaze closely
imitating that of T'ang pottery (fig. 233). The provenance of
this last piece is uncertain.

Bizen ware is made at Imbe, in the province of Bizen, in
southern Hondo. The industry dates from the end of the fourteenth century, when rough domestic wares were made of a red
stoneware with a natural glaze or smear.

A visit of the Taiko Hideyoshi in 1583 was followed by a rapid
development of the Imbe manufacture. Tea-ware was now made
and the natural glaze was replaced by an intentional glaze of

[1] See p. 130.

a thin diaphanous kind.[1] The potters were perhaps influenced to some extent by the Chinese Ihing (see p. 42) stoneware. The Imbe ware of this time is called Imbe yaki or ko-Bizen. A slate-coloured or bluish-brown ware made first in the seventeenth century is known as *ao-Bizen* (blue Bizen). Fine figure-modelling is a feature of the Imbe manufacture, the best period for this

FIG. 234. Bizen stoneware duck: 18th century.
H. 14 in.

work being in the eighteenth century. All the old types are copied in modern times.

The specimens shown include two rough bottles of the fourteenth-century type; a saké bottle of the slaty blue (*ao*) ware; and the more usual Bizen wares with grey or red stoneware body, red on the surface, with a thin lustrous glaze often spotted or splashed with opaque tea-green. Specimens of Bizen figures (fig. 234) are exhibited in the middle section, and there is a large and well-modelled figure of Hotei, God of Contentment, standing free on a pedestal (fig. 213).

[1] The Bizen glaze is somewhat similar in appearance to the salt-glaze on English stoneware; and it is said that the potters threw seaweed on to the fuel in the kiln when the ware was glowing.

The *Kioto* potteries are numerous and important, and their history dates from the early part of the sixteenth century, when a Corean named Ameya settled in the district. His family, which was represented in the year 1900 by the thirteenth generation, is famous for the *Raku* ware. This pottery, which from the time of Ameya's son Chojiro (flourished about 1580) has been popular in the form of tea-bowls, incense-boxes, and other utensils for the tea ceremony, no less than for domestic use, is as a rule hand-modelled, but sometimes thrown, sometimes carved, or again both thrown and carved; and for the reason that it can be very easily fired, it has been made by numerous amateur and professional potters. There are two distinct sorts of Raku ware, *kuro*, or black, and *aka*, or red. The former is made of a mixture of fine and coarse clay or of clay and pounded biscuit. It is glazed with a powdered stone, rich in iron, taken from the bed of the river Kamo, and lead oxide, and is fired at a temperature of about 1100° C. Its normal colour ranges from black to dark reddish brown. *Aka-raku* is made simply of red clay, sometimes partly covered with white slip under a waxy, more or less transparent lead glaze.

FIG. 235. Incense-box in form of a sparrow: grey and red glaze: marked *raku*. L. 2·5 in.

It is a soft earthenware, fired at about 850° C., and the salmon-pink colour is that of the body showing through the glaze. Sometimes a black slip was used as decoration, occasionally pieces were dappled with copper-green or, as was also done in the case of black raku, painted with various coloured slips. Raku ware found favour with Sen no Rikiu, the greatest of the tea-masters, and with the Taiko Hideyoshi, in the sixteenth century; the latter granted a seal, inscribed *raku* (enjoyment), to Chojiro. Some of the most celebrated Raku tea-bowls were made by Honami Koetsu in the first half of the seventeenth century.

A variety of *raku* wares (fig. 235) are shown among the representatives of other factories which imitated the type. A honey-coloured kind called Ohi ware has been made in the province of Kaga since the end of the seventeenth century.

There are *Kioto* tea-jars and bowls in Seto style of an early type, made by amateurs from the sixteenth century onwards; but the most important ceramic development of the district was the manufacture of an earthenware with greyish body and crackled yellowish glaze which was at first decorated with sketchy designs in blue and brown. From this grew the typical *Awata* 'cream ware', used by many noted potters and the staple of the district to this day. The names of *Ninsei* and *Kenzan* add lustre to the Kioto annals. Nomura *Seisuke*, whose native village is by the temple of *Nin*waji, was a pupil of Sohaku, a master of tea ceremonies. He took the art name of Ninsei, and his earliest ceramic efforts were made in the brown-painted 'cream ware'. About 1655, having learnt the art of enamelling from a Hizen potter, he started making enamelled earthenware, working in the Omura district, at Awata, Iwakura, and Mizoro (districts of Kioto), and teaching his secrets to the local potters. Ninsei improved the local ware, refining the body material and the crackled glaze, and, besides introducing the art of enamel painting, he shook off foreign influence and started a national style of decoration which became typical of Japanese pottery. The mark of Ninsei is common, but genuine specimens of his work are virtually unknown out of Japan. There are specimens of his style of enamelled decoration in the Collection; and it will be seen that he used gold, silver, red, and enamels on a crackled cream glaze. Other glazes used were pearl-white with a pink tinge, golden brown, chocolate, buff, and metallic black.

Ogata Sansei, whose art name is *Kenzan* (b. 1660, d. 1743), was brother of the famous artist Korin. He worked at Awata, using the ordinary body materials and glazes on which he painted simple but bold designs of an exceedingly tasteful and harmonious kind—a prunus branch, a floral scroll, a flight of geese, a suggestion of flowers and trees, or a vigorous landscape sketch. Though a master of all methods of decoration, he preferred brown and blue painting to the enamels. Kenzan also worked for a time at Yedo. The mark of Kenzan (which has the same ideographs as Inu-yama) appears on several specimens in the Collection. But it is highly improbable that any of them were the work of Ogata Sansei. Imitations, of course, abound; but it must be remembered that the Kenzan mark was used by descendants of the great potter down to the nineteenth century.

Other prominent names associated with the Awata ware are Kinkozan, Hozan, Taizan, and Dohachi. These potters all worked in the eighteenth century and left descendants who have carried on their potteries to the present day.

Kinkozan, appointed court potter in 1756, is credited with changing the body of Awata ware from brown to light buff and with perfection in enamelling: two good examples of Kinkozan enamelled ware (fig. 238) are shown.

Hozan (d. 1720) specialized in landscapes and floral-scroll designs in underglaze blue and slip. Hozan was a master in the use of slips (liquid clay). His wares are very varied. They include imitations of Dutch Delft; and the 'fern-scroll style'

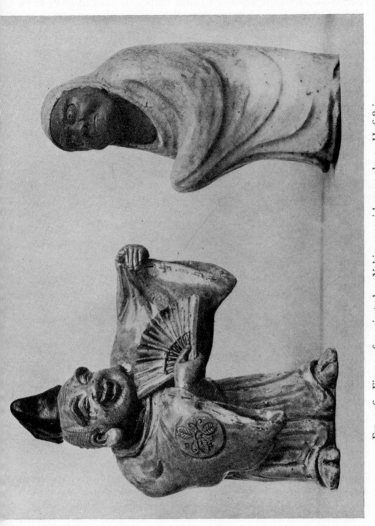

Fig. 236. Figure of a minstrel as Yebis: greenish grey glaze. H. 6·8 in.
Fig. 237. Figure of Daruma: grey *raku* glaze.

(*warabi-de*), seen on a tea-bowl and teapot, is said to have been originated by one of his family in the eighteenth century.

Taizan came to Awata in 1711, and worked in the prevailing styles of the district.

Dohachi, a pupil of Eisen, worked at Awata from about 1755 to 1804. He painted in the naturalistic style of the artist Maruyama Okyo, taking his designs from birds, landscape, flowers, &c. Among the more modern potters of the district *Tanzan* seems to have been one of the most prolific.

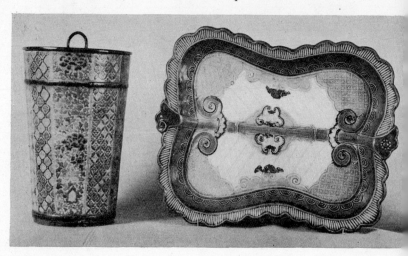

Fig. 238. Enamelled water-jar, marked *kinkozan*. H. 7·8 in.
Fig. 239. Fan-shaped tray with green, yellow, and purple glazes: Minato or Sanuki ware.

The wares made in the Mizoro and Iwakura districts were very similar to those of Awata, viz. crackled cream-glazed earthenware profusely enamelled in a dull blue, red, green, and gold, largely with diaper patterns. The potteries in the Kyomizu and Gojo districts of Kioto made other types of ware, and the term *Kyomizu yaki* is generally used to cover Kioto wares other than those of Awata, Iwakura, and Mizoro.

The first Kyomizu potter had the art name of Ebisei, and his two pupils Eisen, an amateur, and Rokubei, who set up a pottery in 1764, gained great distinction. Eisen made the first Kioto porcelain about 1760, and Rokubei decorated pottery in the Dohachi style.

Later Mokubei, a pupil of Eisen, gained a reputation as a clever copyist; Shuhei for enamelled wares; and Kentei for unglazed pottery with pictorial designs in gold and enamels. An early nineteenth-century potter of high repute was Zengoro Hozen, son of Ryozen; he made pottery of various kinds, but his chief successes were in porcelain (q.v.). He marked his wares with the seal *Eiraku*, the characters of which are the same as those of the Chinese *Yung Lo*. A very large number of potteries were started at Kioto in the last half of the nineteenth century, but there is not space to discuss their productions. The excellent figure of a minstrel (fig. 236) has the mark of a potter named *Shun-yetsu*, but whether he worked at Kioto or Seto is not certain. The Kioto potters made many imitations of foreign wares and old types. There are, for instance, several pieces copied from the Corean *mishima* ware, one of which is signed by a late nineteenth-century Gojo potter named Zoroku; and there is an enamelled dessert basket with moulded vine decoration which is evidently copied from an English original.[1] It has a mark which may perhaps be that of Zoroku, but the writing is indistinct. A specimen of the shrivelled, grey shark-skin glaze is probably of Kioto make; but the pieces beside it were made at *Wakayama*, in the province of Kishiu, in southern Hondo. The industry was started here by the feudal chief of the district in a private kiln about 1810, and Zengoro Hozen was invited from Kioto to assist in 1827. The ware varies from porcelain to stoneware and pottery, and it was noted for its turquoise, yellow, purple, and green glazes. The marks used were *Kairakuyen*, and *Kahin Shiriu* and *Eiraku*, two seals of Zengoro. The private factory closed in 1844; but other factories were started at Otokoyama in the same neighbourhood, and at Ota, near Yokohama, to make wares of a similar kind. From the specimens exhibited it will be seen that the Ming 'three-colour' ware (q.v.) was closely copied, but it will also be noticed that the Kishiu wares often have an unpleasantly damp and sticky surface due to excess of soda in the glaze.

A series of baskets and trays are made of a fine, pale buff ware with coloured glazes (green, yellow, aubergine, &c.) in the style of a Southern Chinese pottery to which the Japanese have given the name of 'Kochi ware'. The designs are moulded in low relief or outlined in thread-like lines and filled in with washes of colour, or again the coloured glazes are applied in broad areas without any containing lines.

Some of this ware was made at *Minato*, in the province of Izumi, where old potteries existed at the end of the seventeenth century; but it was also made on the Island of *Awaji* where a factory was started in 1830, and in the province of *Sanuki*.

Another ware of strong individuality is the *Yatsushiro* stoneware. It is as a rule of grey colour, though the edges of the foot-rim are burnt brown; and the typical decoration is in white slip,

[1] The same model is seen in eighteenth-century Staffordshire salt-glaze and Chelsea and Worcester porcelains.

either brushed on or inlaid in the style of the Corean *mishima*,
under a transparent pearl-grey glaze. The ground colour is
sometimes a brown which was probably produced by a dressing
of slip. Yatsushiro is in the province of Higo, in the Island of
Kiushiu, and the industry was started there by a Corean in the
early years of the seventeenth century. Most of the examples in
the Collection are of recent date.

JAPANESE PORCELAIN

(*BAY VIII and the TABLE-CASE OF BAY VII*)

THE first porcelain made in Japan was that of Gorodayu go
Shonzui, but it was not Japanese porcelain. According to the
traditional account, Shonzui went to Kingtehchen in 1510 and
studied there for five years. He brought back to Japan a knowledge of the Chinese blue and white porcelain and a supply of
Chinese materials, which included, it is said, some of the precious
Mohammedan blue. With this stock-in-trade, tradition says, he
established himself in Hizen, in the Island of Kiushiu, in the
neighbourhood of Arita; and though he must have worked almost
under the shadow of Izumi-yama, afterwards so celebrated for
its porcelain stone, he failed to find the requisite materials in
Japan, and his porcelain was limited to what he was able to make
before his Chinese supplies were exhausted. Reputed specimens
of Shonzui's porcelain are blue and white of the Chinese Ming
type, but often with the addition of passages of diaper patterns
in Japanese taste. It is, of course, excessively rare and precious
to-day, and it has been very well imitated both in Japan and
China. It is extremely improbable that any specimen of it has
reached this country. A bottle-shaped sprinkler (fig. 241) has
been attributed to Shonzui. It is certainly well designed to look
the part, and it may at any rate be regarded as representing the
Shonzui type.

Shonzui is said to have died about 1550, and some five-and-fifty
years later the deposits of porcelain stone on Izumi-yama were
found by a Corean immigrant named Risampei. A factory was
established at Arita and the manufacture of true Japanese porcelain began. The Arita stone is of a peculiar nature, containing
elements of both kaolin and petuntse in such a condition that it
can be used alone to make porcelain without admixture of any
other material. But it is difficult to manage and apt to be coarse;
and great labour was required to ensure a fine ware. The earliest
Arita porcelain, as recognized from fragments excavated on the
site of the kilns, was painted in underglaze blue and rudimentary
green and red enamels; and it was not till about 1660 that the

PLATE XIX

Fig. 240. Kaga vase: 17th century. H. 11·8 in.

FIG. 241. Blue and white
sprinkler: style of Shonzui.
H. 8·3 in.

FIG. 242. Arita dish in Kakiemon style:
17th century. D. 8·5 in.

FIG. 243. Arita bottle in
Kakiemon style: 17th
century. H. 8·6 in.

FIG. 244. Arita figure of a boy,
Kakiemon style: 17th century.
H. 10 in.

beautiful enamelling, for which the ware is chiefly noted, was perfected. A potter named Sakaida Kakiemon is credited with this development, and he is said to have obtained some help from a Chinese friend. The chief Kakiemon enamels are a soft orange-red, a grass-green, and lilac-blue; and to these may be added a pale primrose-yellow, turquoise-green, gold, and occasionally underglaze blue. But the designs used are more notable than

FIG. 245. 'Imari' dish: about 1700. D. 15 in.

the enamels. They are slight and elegant and in the best Japanese taste, leaving plenty of scope to the white porcelain ground when it was pure enough to deserve prominence. A few blossoms, a floral medallion, a flowering prunus tree, a banded hedge with birds, quails and millet, a tiger and bamboos, a dragon, or children are the motives of slight but nicely balanced designs. The porcelain itself is subject to wide variations. At its best it is pure milk-white with a glaze of close texture and a rather greasy sheen. Inferior specimens are greyish, and the glaze is apt to craze and become discoloured. Another artist of this school, known by signed specimens,[1] is Shibuemon, uncle of the sixth Kakiemon (*fl.* 1695–9).

The Dutch, who were allowed to establish a settlement on the

---

[1] See *Oriental Ceramics*, 1929, vol. ii, no. 2.

island of Deshima, off Nagasaki, in the year 1641, very soon
found that this ware had a good market in Europe, and it was
imported in considerable quantity. Old catalogues call it the
première qualité coloriée de Japon, and it was freely copied by the
potters at Delft and the porcelain-makers at St. Cloud, Mennecy,
Meissen, Bow, Chelsea, and elsewhere. But apparently the Dutch

FIGS. 246, 247, and 248. 'Imari' vase (H. 26 in.) and two beakers:
17th century.

taste craved for something more florid than the Kakiemon wares;
and the story is that one of their company, Sieur Wagenaar,
suggested a heavier decoration based on brocade patterns.
Whatever the truth of this story, there certainly was a second
and entirely different type of ware made at Arita solely for the
European trade. More often than not the porcelain of this group
is heavy, coarse, and greyish, but its roughness is concealed by
masses of dark, cloudy blue set off with Indian red and gilding.
These colours are supplemented by green, yellow, and aubergine
and occasionally by a brownish black which is distinct from the
greenish black of the Chinese *famille verte*; and the designs,
irregular and confused, consist of asymmetrical panels surrounded
by mixed brocade patterns. This ware enjoyed great popularity

FIG. 249. 'Imari' bowl: about 1700. D. 10·4 in.

FIG. 250. Arita bottle: about 1700. H. 8·5 in.

in Europe, where it was distinguished as 'old Imari'.[1] There is much of it in the Dresden Collection, which dates from about 1700, including large vases which have been heavily lacquered. A coarser kind of lacquered Imari was made in the last half of the nineteenth century and shipped to Europe under the name of Nagasaki ware.

But all the Imari porcelain was not destined for export. There

FIG. 251. 'Imari' bowl with European figures. D. 10·7 in.

were finer types with Japanese devices such as the chrysanthemum badge (*kikumon*) and the *paulownia* leaf (*kirimon*), embedded in the blue, red, and gold decoration; and other wares with more restrained decoration such as the incense-burners which came with the Sloane Collection in 1753 (fig. 252). In these superior pieces the ware is purer and whiter, the blue better, and the red richer and more opaque.

We have already seen (p. 78) that both the Kakiemon and 'old Imari' wares were closely copied by the Chinese. Indeed this 'Chinese Imari' is often mistaken for Japanese work; but there are many points of difference. The crisp, clean Chinese porcelain with smooth greenish oily glaze and biscuit slightly

---

[1] Imari is the seaport of Arita.

M

browned at the foot-rim differs sharply from the Japanese, which is usually heavier and greyer (though sometimes a dead white) and with a glaze of coarser texture, full of minute pin-holes which give it almost a muslin-like appearance. The Japanese porcelain was supported on small pointed 'spurs' in the kiln and the marks of these supports are generally visible; and, contrary to the Chinese custom, the body of the ware was submitted to a preliminary firing ('biscuited'), which circumstance no doubt affected the appearance of the underglaze blue. At any rate, the Imari blue was apt to run and become 'frayed' at the edges,

FIG. 252. Arita incense-burner, painted in black and gold: Sloane Coll. H. 2·8 in.

a defect which was carefully concealed by the red and gold decoration applied to the finished glaze. The actual tone of the Imari blue is different from that of the Chinese, being darker, less pure, and lacking in the marbled depths of the latter; and the iron-red of the Imari is more opaque than the Chinese coral tint and sometimes has the appearance of sealing-wax. This thick, opaque red is specially characteristic of the later wares.

A good series of Arita porcelains is shown in Bay VIII, Cases A, B, C, D, G, H, and K, and in the Table-case of Bay VII. The Kakiemon types are mostly exhibited in Cases B, top, and C: there are specimens of the old Imari in Cases G, H, and K, and of the better class of Imari (that with Japanese badges, &c.) in Cases A and B.

The Collection shows that the Arita porcelain was not confined to the ordinary 'Imari' types. It includes blue and white; monochromes of celadon green, dark blue (*ruri*) which is sometimes gilt, violet aubergine, and lustrous brown (fig. 253); embossed ware, white and coloured, pierced work and figures modelled in the round (fig. 244).

Other celebrated Hizen porcelains are the Okawachi and Mikawachi wares. The factory of *Okawachi*, eight miles from Arita, was founded in 1660 by the feudal chief Nabeshima, prince of Saga. He took the best workmen from the early factories at Hirose and Ichinoe which had been started about 1600 by Corean and Arita potters. Materials from Arita were used and a porcelain of fine quality was made, chiefly for the prince's own use. At the end of the eighteenth century the princely support was gradually withdrawn, local materials were used and the ware deteriorated.

FIG. 253. Arita bowl with brown and white prunus on a brown glaze. D. 6·2 in.

The early Nabeshima porcelain is a good white ware with lustrous glaze of fine texture, decorated in Kakiemon style in enamels with or without underglaze blue. Another characteristic Nabeshima ware is painted with branches of cherry blossom, maple leaves, &c., naturalistically rendered in underglaze blue with touches of enamels—chiefly pale bluish green and deep orange red: and another has similar designs in an underglaze blue which is light and soft but rather thin. Bowls and dishes with deep foot-rims often have a comb pattern (*kushi-de*) as a border for these parts. Early specimens are very rare, and consequently much importance attaches to a plate (fig. 254), with the mark of the Dresden Collection. The Dresden inventory shows that this piece was added to the collection in 1721. The colours with which it is decorated are underglaze blue and overglaze enamel blue, turquoise green, pale yellow, and soft opaque red. Celadon-green porcelain was also made at Okawachi.

The first *Mikawachi* pottery was started by Coreans about 1650; but it was not till the deposits of fine porcelain stone on the island of Amakusa had been discovered in 1712 that porcelain was attempted. In 1751 the factory was taken under the patronage of Matsura, prince of Hirado; and from 1751 to 1843 the finest porcelain of Japan was made at Mikawachi. It was mostly reserved for the prince and little came into the market till the

FIG. 254. Nabeshima plate from the Dresden Coll. D. 8·5 in.

middle of the nineteenth century. The Hirado porcelain is milk-white and as fine as pipe-clay, with pure, velvet-like glaze, lustrous and of the finest texture. The potting is perfection, and the decoration, as a rule neatly pencilled in a pale, delicate blue, consists mainly of landscapes, figures, trees, and flowers—a favourite design representing Chinese boys (three, five, or seven in number) at play under a pine tree (fig. 256). The potters excelled in moulded, carved, and pierced designs and in modelling figures in the round. The latter were sometimes decorated in coloured glazes. No mark was used on the wares made for the prince: those made for the market often bore the name of the factory and the potter; but these were generally a lower-grade ware.

A few specimens in Bay VIII illustrate the general character of the ware, but they do not belong to the early period.

The Amakusa stone was also used at a factory opened in 1803 at Kameyama, near Nagasaki. A few specimens of this ware are shown, and they will be seen to be decorated in underglaze blue (in some cases, of a decidedly mauve tint) in the Chinese Ming style. With them is the sprinkler reputed to be a specimen of Shonzui's work (p. 156).

An important porcelain industry flourished in the province of *Kaga*, in western Hondo, at Kutani, and other places. Porcelain stone was found here about 1650, and the prince of Kaga ordered

FIG. 255. Hirado box in form of a duck: mark of Imagawa Bunjiro. L. 5 in.

FIG. 256. Hirado blue and white bowl with pine tree and five boys. H. 2·5 in.

Goto Saijiro and another potter to start a factory. They were not successful until Goto had visited Arita and learnt the art there in 1664. Several types of early Kaga ware can be distinguished: (1) *Ao-Kutani* (green Kutani) which was decorated in green, yellow, purple, and soft Prussian blue enamels in broad washes over black outlines either on the biscuit or on the glaze, the green enamel predominating; (2) a porcelain painted in Arita style in green, red, aubergine, yellow, and blue enamels, silver and gold and, rarely, underglaze blue; and (3) *Ko-Kutani* (old Kutani) on which red predominated, generally in diaper patterns separating enamelled medallions. Sometimes large areas were covered with red, and the rest painted in green, silver, or gold. The Kutani red is 'a peculiarly soft, subdued, opaque colour, varying from Indian red to russet brown'.

The ware itself varies from stoneware through semi-porcelain and ordinary white porcelain to delicate eggshell: and the glaze is usually lustreless and mat and sometimes crazed in parts. The Kutani factory apparently ceased to produce good wares about 1750.

There were, however, many revivals: (1) in the Nomi district which started in 1779, the wares being chiefly in the Ao-Kutani

and Arita styles; (2) in the Enuma district in the early part of
the nineteenth century. Here Ao-Kutani methods were followed;
and about 1840 a potter named Iida Hachiroemon introduced,
or at any rate popularized, the decoration in red and gold (*akaji-kinga*) which is probably the type of Kaga ware best known in
Europe. This *hachiro-e* decoration is generally on a soft creamy
ware with crazed or crackled glaze. A short-lived attempt to
revive the industry in the village of Kutani was made by Danemon

FIG. 257. Kaga bottle in
Arita style: 17th century.
H. 11·3 in.

FIG. 258. Red and green
Kaga food vessel: made in
sections. H. 11 in.

Toyoda (called Yoshidaya) from 1824 to 1826. The kiln was
subsequently removed to Yamashiro.[1]

Still more recently there has been a revival of the Ao-Kutani
ware; but the modern specimens are chiefly on a stoneware body.
It should be added that factories in other parts of Japan occasionally sent their wares to Kaga for decoration.

The marks used previously to 1850 were only *Kutani* and the
seal form of the character *fuku* (happiness): potters' names appear
on the modern wares. Examples of most of the Kaga types are
shown. The *Ao* enamels and the Arita style are well illustrated
by a fine vase and bottle (figs. 240 and 257), the latter of a
characteristic Kaga shape: the Ko-Kutani by a multiple food-
vessel of bottle shape (fig. 258) in the middle section: the *hachiro-e*
style in red and gold by a large bowl in the lower part; and

[1] See *Oriental Ceramics*, 1929, vol. ii, no. 5.

PLATE XX

FIG. 259. Koto incense-burner enamelled in colours. H. 6·8 in.

there are several large dishes, bowls, &c., mostly of recent date, but illustrating the deep, rich qualities of the *Ao* enamels and glazes.

A few *Kioto* porcelains are exhibited in Bay VIII. Porcelain was first made in the Kyomizu district by Eisen about 1760. The late Ming red and green family served as a model for decoration. Mokubei and Dohachi were pupils of Eisen. Ogata Shuhei at the end of the century was distinguished for a brilliantly enamelled porcelain, and he is said to have first used the red and gold decoration at Kioto. Another distinguished potter, who used similar methods, was Eiraku (an art-name of Zengoro Hozen), to whom we have already referred (p. 155). He worked at various factories till his death in 1855, and his descendants still carry on the business, using the seal *Eiraku*. There are several bowls with his marks in the Collection. They are of a studied roughness of shape. The list of Kioto porcelain-makers is a long one and includes the names of Rokubei, Rantei, Seifu, Kitei, Kanzan, and Makuzu Kozan. Makuzu's grandson, who worked near Yokohama, was perhaps the most distinguished modern Japanese potter.

The *Koto* incense-burner in the same section is an exceptionally good specimen of Japanese enamelled porcelain (fig. 259). It was made at a factory on the shore of Lake Biwa (Koto means 'east of the lake') which was active from 1830 to 1860. The Koto porcelain has a peculiarly soft, lustrous, oily glaze which is very Chinese in appearance, and it is decorated in blue and white, or in good enamels—sometimes in green and red in Ming style.

A small series of Japanese celadons shows how closely this type of Chinese ware was copied in Japan, where the old Sung specimens were treated with an almost reverential respect. Celadon was made at the Arita, Okawachi, Kioto, and other factories; but it was a specialty of the Sanda pottery established in the Arima district of Settsu in the nineteenth century. The material found in this district was peculiarly suitable for the celadon ware, and the paste of the Sanda celadon has much similarity to that of the Chinese ware of Lungchüan. There was also a factory at Himeji, in the province of Harima, where celadon and blue and white porcelains were made with materials from Tozan hill.

The Table-case of Bay VII is mainly furnished with smaller specimens of Japanese porcelain made at various factories, some of which have been already discussed. There are specimens of Awaji (see p. 155) porcelain with coloured glazes in Chinese style, including 'egg and spinach' and tortoise-shell: a series of Kioto celadon water-droppers with Zodiac animals on top; and a few pieces of Kishiu ware: examples of the use of lacquer and cloisonné enamel on pottery and porcelain: small pieces of blue and white ware made at various factories including a box with a well-modelled figure of a boy with Hotei's bag (fig. 260), possibly of Hirado make; and examples of Japanese eggshell porcelain.

Blue and white porcelain was extensively made in the nineteenth century at *Seto*, in Owari, the industry having been started by Kato Tamikichi who brought back the secrets of the manufacture from Hizen in 1807; and a very similar ware was

FIG. 260.   Blue and white incense-box.
? Hirado.   D. 2·4 in.

made in the province of *Mino*. Some of the Japanese 'eggshell' porcelain shows remarkable manipulative skill. The factories celebrated in the nineteenth century for this delicate ware are those of Mikawachi, Seto, Shiba, Mino, and Yamato. *Shiba* is near Tokio, and the fine pinky white eggshell made here was richly decorated at the Tokio enamelling establishments: it is often cased in delicate basket-work. Another striking object in this section is the white porcelain bowl, with moulded relief designs inside, shaped and finished in the style of the old Chinese ware; and there is an assortment of the smaller Hizen porcelains, some of which are of high quality (fig. 253).

MARKS

THE mark is usually found under the base of the vessel, though occasionally it appears on the side or lip. In most cases it is painted in underglaze blue and enclosed in a double ring. This is particularly true of the earlier wares; but, in the eighteenth century and after, painting the mark in enamel colours and even in gold became more common. Sometimes the mark is stamped on the body with a seal. The usual form of writing is the ordinary script, though other characters are also used, especially when the mark is put in a square frame to look like the imprint of a seal. If a number of characters are used, they are ranged in parallel columns which are read from top to bottom, the columns being taken from right to left.

Chinese marks may be classified as: (1) Date marks; (2) Hall-marks; (3) Marks of commendation, felicitation, &c.; (4) Signa-tures; (5) Symbols.

(1) The commonest form of date mark is the *nien hao* (reign name) of the Emperor. It is usually in six characters, e.g. *ta ming ch'êng hua nien chih* = made (*chih*) in the period (*nien*) Ch'êng Hua of the Great Ming (dynasty): but the two first characters which

FIG. 261.

give the name of the dynasty are occasionally omitted. The ordinary *nien hao* which occur in the Collection are given on pp. 172 and 173. Seal characters are not uncommon in the reign-marks of the eighteenth century and later: fig. 261 is the seal-mark of the Ch'ien Lung period in four characters.

It has already been observed that this kind of date mark cannot always (or indeed very often) be accepted at its face value. The Chinese made a practice of placing on their wares the names of emperors whose reigns were noted for ceramic excellence. Thus a great quantity of K'ang Hsi porcelain bears the reign name of Hsüan Tê or Ch'êng Hua, and one of the commonest marks on modern wares is that of K'ang Hsi. The names of late and inferior periods were not so likely to be used in this way; and it is generally assumed that the correct reign mark would be put on the wares made for Imperial use, but even this cannot be regarded as a fixed rule.

Another form of dating is by the *cyclical* system. Beginning from 2637 B.C. time is reckoned in cycles of sixty years, and each year has a name composed of two characters, i.e. one of the 'ten stems' combined with one of 'twelve branches'.[1] The cyclical dates give the exact year of the cycle, but very often there is nothing to indicate the actual cycle concerned, except the internal evidence of the ware. If, however, the cyclical date is combined with a *nien hao*, then we have a method of dating

---

[1] There is no space to explain these obscure terms; but they will be found set out, with the characters, in most books of reference: such as W. F. Mayers, *Chinese Readers' Manual.*

as precise as our own. An interesting example of a cyclical date occurs on fig. 262, viz. *yu hsin ch'ou nien chih* = made in the *hsin-ch'ou* year recurring. The *hsin-ch'ou* is the 38th year of the cycle and it actually did recur in the reign of K'ang Hsi who completed a full cycle of reign in the year 1721.[1]

(2) Hall-marks are so called because they usually contain the character *t'ang* (hall) which may refer to a studio, workshop or factory, the name of a private house, or a shop, a family- or art-name of an artist, or a pavilion in a palace. The Chinese artist usually has an art-name which contains some allusion to his studio or dwelling; and in the place of *t'ang* we sometimes find

FIG. 262.

other characters such as *t'ing* (summer house), *chai* (studio), *hsüan* (terrace), or *fang* (retreat).

(3) Marks of commendation, &c., include a single word or phrase praising the ware, e.g. *yü* (jade), *pao shêng* (of unique value); a good wish for the possessor, e.g. *shou* (long life), *fu* (happiness), or, more subtly, *tan kuei* (red cassia) which is an emblem of literary success; an aphorism, or any phrase of benevolent meaning.

(4) Signatures (as distinct from hall-marks) of potters or decorators are very rare on Kingtehchen porcelain, but more common on the pottery and porcelain made elsewhere.

(5) Symbols, rebuses, &c., are sometimes put in place of the written mark. They include the sacred Buddhist Emblems (the shell, wheel, umbrella, vase, angular knot, &c.), the Emblems of the Immortals, the Eight Precious Things (pearl, cash, lozenge, musical stone, artemisia leaf, &c.), the bat (symbol of happiness), the fungus, stork (fig. 263), and hare (symbols of long life), &c. These symbol marks are frequently found on K'ang Hsi blue and white; and it is interesting to read that in 1677 the district magistrate forbade the Kingtehchen potters to put the Emperor's name on their porcelain. This prohibition may have been in force for some years and may account for the habit of leaving

[1] It should be explained that in calculating the initial dates of their reigns Chinese Emperors did not mention the year in which their predecessor died. Thus the date of K'ang Hsi is given as 1662–1722, but he actually succeeded to the throne in 1661.

the double ring empty or filled with a symbol instead of a reign-mark.

A few examples of the various marks are given on pp. 172 and 173, but those in the Collection are far too numerous to be reproduced in full in a Handbook.[1]

Marks on Japanese pottery and porcelain are in principle the same as on the Chinese. Corresponding with the *nien hao* are the Japanese *nengo*,[2] period names, which began in A.D. 645; the Chinese cyclical dates are used without alteration; there are hall-marks, which are obviously art-names, such as *Ko-tei* (lake house); marks of felicitation occur occasionally, such as *fuku* (happiness) and *jiu* (long life) on Arita and Kaga porcelains; and

FIG. 263.

there are vast numbers of potters' seals and signatures. As already noted, the Japanese potteries were mostly small, family concerns; and the potters jealously preserved their individuality. Their marks are consequently legion, and the numbers are further increased by the fact that successful artists were accorded various seals and art-names. Kenzan, for instance, has a round dozen of these pseudonyms and Zengoro Hozen at least three.

It is manifestly impossible to reproduce all the marks in the Collection in a Handbook; but a few of the more important are appended on p. 174.

It should be added that Chinese reign names, especially those of Ming emperors, are not uncommon on the porcelain of Arita and other places, and that Japanese marks and inscriptions are written with the Chinese ideographs, though they are pronounced with very different sounds. An instance, already mentioned, is the name *Eiraku* which represents the Chinese *Yung Lo*; another is the character meaning 'made', which rounds off both the Chinese and Japanese marks; it is read *chih*, if Chinese, *sei* or *tsukuru*, if Japanese. Japanese marks sometimes end in a flourish, known as a *kakihan* (written seal), which is, of course, untranslatable.

---

[1] Most of them will be found in the *Catalogue of the Franks Collection*, 1878, and in Burton and Hobson, *Marks on Pottery and Porcelain*, London, 1928.

[2] A list of the *nengo* from 1370 to 1868 is given in Burton and Hobson, op. cit., p. 157.

MING REIGN-MARKS

洪武 年製   Hung Wu (1368–98)

永樂 年製   Yung Lo (1403–24)

大明宣德年製   Hsüan Tê (1426–35)

大明成化年製   Ch'êng Hua (1465–87)

大明弘治年製   Hung Chih (1488–1505)

大明正德年製   Chêng Tê (1506–21)

大明嘉靖年製   Chia Ching (1522–66)

大明隆慶年製   Lung Ch'ing (1567–72)

大明萬曆年製   Wan Li (1573–1619)

大明天啟年製   T'ien Ch'i (1621–7)

大明崇禎年製   Ch'ung Chêng (1628–44)

CH'ING REIGN-MARKS

大清順治年製   Shun Chih (1644–61)

大清康熙年製   K'ang Hsi (1662–1722)

大清雍正年製   Yung Chêng (1723–35)

大清乾隆年製   Ch'ien Lung (1736–95)

年製 嘉慶 Chia Ch'ing (1796-1820)

光年製 大清道 Tao Kuang (1821-50)

豐年製 大清咸 Hsien Fêng (1851-61)

治年製 大清同 T'ung Chih (1862-74)

緒年製 大清光 Kuang Hsü (1875-1908)

HALL-MARKS

佳器 玉堂 Yü t'ang chia ch'i (beautiful vessel for the jade hall)

博古製 慎德堂 Shên tê t'ang po ku chih (antique made at the Shên-tê hall)

玉宝勝 yü (jade)

pao shêng (of unique value)

Chiang ming kao tsao (made by Chiang Ming-kao)

'Shop mark'

? Importer's mark

hare

Fuku (happiness) on Japanese porcelain

Fuku (happiness) on Japanese porcelain

Raku

 Dai Nippon
Seto tsukuru

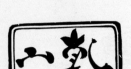 Kenzan

 Banko

 Fuyeki

 Eiraku

 Banko

 Ninsei

 Soma

 Taizan

 Dohachi

 Akahada

 Kanzan
sei sei

 Kinkozan

 Asahi

 Hozan

 Kutani

 Makuzu
Kozan
tsukuru

PRESENT LOCATIONS

INDEX